CW00542120

THE
Person
IN THE BED

How do you deal with the suffering of
hospital patients and their families,
their wants and needs?
Here is what I learned over forty-two years
in the intensive care unit.

Debra Bauguess

The Person in the Bed

Trilogy Christian Publishers
A Wholly Owned Subsidary of Trinity Broadcasting Network
2442 Michelle Drive Tustin, CA 92780

Copyright © 2022 by Debra Bauguess

All Scripture quotations are from the Holy Bible, New International Version®, NIV®. Copyright © 1973, 1978, 1984, 2011 by Biblica, Inc.™ Used by permission of Zondervan. All rights reserved worldwide. www.zondervan.com. The "NIV" and "New International Version" are trademarks registered in the United States Patent and Trademark Office by Biblica, Inc. ™

No part of this book may be reproduced, stored in a retrieval system, or transmitted by any means without written permission from the author. All rights reserved. Printed in the USA. Rights Department, 2442 Michelle Drive, Tustin, CA 92780.

Trilogy Christian Publishing/TBN and colophon are trademarks of Trinity Broadcasting Network. For information about special discounts for bulk purchases, please contact Trilogy Christian Publishing.

Trilogy Disclaimer: The views and content expressed in this book are those of the author and may not necessarily reflect the views and doctrine of Trilogy Christian Publishing or the Trinity Broadcasting Network.

Manufactured in the United States of America
10 9 8 7 6 5 4 3 2 1
Library of Congress Cataloging-in-Publication Data is available.

ISBN: 978-1-68556-324-0
E-ISBN: 978-1-68556-325-7

DEDICATED TO

All caregivers, especially ICU registered nurses (RNs).

To my mom, dad, brother, and aunt, who loved me unconditionally and put up with years of crazy shift days and hours.

To all the thousands of patients and their families who trusted me and "let me in." We laughed, cried, prayed, hugged, and loved together.

To all my frontline heroes: central supply, housekeeping, pharmacy, dieticians, cafeteria workers, occupational therapists, speech therapists, physical therapists, case managers, social workers, chaplains, engineers, respiratory therapists; computerized tomography, X-ray, MRI, EKG, ultrasound, and echo techs.

To my mentors and teachers: Margaret Livingston, Debbie Tuggle, Bobbi Squellati, Don Edwards, Bev Ford, Bunkie Mangum, Anne Whittaeker, Chris Frohnen, Dan Russell, and Cindy Sweeney. You taught me and inspired me.

The "Ds": Dot, Diane, Donna, and Denice.

To so many MDs: Lalchandani, Schafer, Hemphill, Ruggles, Karmakar, Anderson, Bayne, Smith, Morrison, Cabrera, Baron, Fisher, Lao, Majetich, Murphy, and Ravuri. Your faith, trust, and friendship meant more than words can say.

Most of all: a thank-you to Jesus, my Lord and Savior, and Pastor Mark. I was given a job that was my passion and mission field. Jesus gave me empathy and compassion. My prayer-warrior friends and Bible study ladies encouraged and prayed for me and gave me the strength to last.

My dream is for this book's concepts to be taught in nursing and medical schools. As far as I know, no nursing or medical school curriculum teaches about the person in the bed and his or her needs.

All proceeds from this book, after covering costs, will go to a Christian organization to feed starving children.

CONTENTS

FOREWORD

You have retired, but your life has revived. I detected that, early on, you discovered your calling and, in so doing, came upon the secret of life and never looked back. It is no mystery how you have been able to share, to give your life away with such poignancy. You became aware of who you are and why God made you the way He did.

Like Christ, you *feel*. Your ability *to feel* enables you to touch and hug, generating the electricity of God's love from one human to another.

"The heavens declare the glory of God" (Psalm 19:1). In a lesser way, so does the ICU.

I see in you a portrait depicting one who "rolls over" such burdens on the Lord. You otherwise would have been crushed to powder.

This book will do so much for the medical field, and I would be surprised if it does not become such a tool and bring lots of understanding to the nurses and doctors and much glory to the Lord.

Finally, my dear friend, a hope and a prayer with regard to you and this book: may this book, like its author, give hope to the hopeless, give a hug and receive a hug, turn anger into gratitude, turn frowns into smiles, provide health and healing, provide a path to a doorway to God's way, shout out with a voice saying, "Give your life to others," arrest the indifferent, capture the heartless, restore faith in human goodness, define someone's calling with a sense of belonging, provide light in the darkest night, become a living text, a manual, a guide to any and all "in search of"; may it be a Divine Positioning System (GPS), helping lost and wandering souls to find their way home.

—Curtis Johnson

Thank you for your faith in me, Curtis Johnson, my dear friend and fellow author.

PREFACE

How does one know the worth of a human life? Did I know I'd shock one man's heart back into a normal rhythm for him to live twenty-one more years? Did I know I'd be: hugging a stranger while her husband died, forcefully telling a doctor to stop a procedure so I could do cardiopulmonary resuscitation (CPR) on his patient, buying a bike for my homeless patient, telling my friend and coworker we'd just finished CPR on her husband who died, or yelling for help while a five-year-old turned blue in front of me?

Did I know I would educate MDs, peers, and students in Advanced Cardiac Life Support, ICU nursing skills, EKGs, or on intra-aortic balloon pumps?

How does one end up in any given job? Does the job choose you, or do you choose the job? Do you choose a job out of necessity, purely for money, or because it's something you love? I loved anatomy and physiology in high school and college. I wanted to help people and wanted a job I could keep for a long time and support myself with.

Nursing became my gift. It increased my sense of self-worth and happiness. It opened my eyes to the true suffering in this world. I saw many, many heartbreaks and miracles most will never see. No job is perfect. Any job will have good days and bad days. It's what you do with all of those days put together that keeps you in it. Nursing is one of those jobs there will always be a need for: weekends, holidays, and twenty-four hours a day. A job is what you make of it. Nursing, being based on dealing with people, will either draw you in or push you away, depending on the types of people and interactions you have. You get what you put into it; it stretches your ability to love as you let God lead you. If it—*good* and *bad*—continues to pull you deeper, you are hooked.

You have to have a passion for helping *all* people. You put up with bad language, mean peers (including MDs), many varieties of body fluids, and lots of blood. You have angry patients in alcohol withdrawal and coming down off meth and narcotics. What you receive is far greater. You get the undying gratitude and love of a desperate family member who will never forget your love, hugs, and compassion in a moment of loss. You will get joy from helping someone who cannot help himself or herself and needs a loving touch from a fellow human being who cares. You treat all colors, races, and religions the same. We are all formed by one Creator.

I started my childhood loving God, and I'll die loving God more. I understand now: I was chosen to be a bedside nurse. I was used as a conduit to pour His love into hurting people. It has never been about me. It has been all about the power of a good and merciful God who led me to a career where He could shine His light and strength through me into the lives of thousands of human beings. The foundation of love has always been and always will be God. These are only maybe fifty stories out of the thousands I cared for. Any caregiver, chaplain, emergency medical technician, paramedic, or police person can find here tips for treating the hurting masses out there if he or she just cares and uses love.

Debra Bauguess

MY QUALIFICATIONS

I went one year and a summer to a junior college (Solano) to get prerequisites out of the way.

I then went to a state college (Chico) for four years and entered the nursing program to get my degrees of bachelor of science in nursing and public health nursing.

In 1978–1979, I worked in the Bay Area, Pinole, on a surgical floor, medical floor, recovery, and ICU.

In 1979–1983, I was in a small Mount Shasta hospital with a four-bed ICU and CCU (coronary care unit). There, I also helped in ER with traumas, delivered babies, and worked the medical-surgical floor.

I spent one month doing night shifts in the Woodland ICU before getting into my last job.

Mercy San Juan Medical Center then hired me for the three to eleven p.m. shift in CCU.

I taught Advanced Cardiac Life Support for about fifteen years.

I was a CCU supervisor for about fifteen years.

I got my CCRN (a highly specialized critical-care certification on my license) and kept that for twenty-two years.

I taught about intra-aortic balloon pumps for Arrow International on the West Coast for about four-plus years (per diem).

I did dobutamine stress tests in a cardiology office for four hours, once a week, for about four years.

I was a teacher of EKGs, critical-care skills, and balloon pumps to peers. My favorite people to teach were the students I mentored, whether they were in first-time nursing programs, already with a different bachelor's degree, or just new to critical care.

I spent most of my years as a coronary care ICU registered nurse (RN) and still love this the most.

The last fourteen years were in a neurological ICU, and our unit was a comprehensive stroke center for a very large area of Northern California. I spent thirty-six years in this last hospital.

FIND A MENTOR

On my first day in Pinole, California, in my first RN job, I met Evelyn, Cecelia, Mike, Dorothy, and Bobbi, all people who had worked there for some time. I was treated with nothing but kindness. I learned fast not to be afraid to ask questions and double-check everything. These were human lives I was now responsible for.

My first mentor, Bobbi, was with me when I lost my first patient. He was an ex-policeman, and I had grown very close to him. Bobbi taught me it was okay to cry when he died in front of me.

She was the one I yelled for when my five-year-old patient, who was a post-op appendectomy, turned gray and started "crowing" with stridor. Bobbi had me immediately shut off the intravenous med that was hanging. A pediatrician in the ER answered the code blue (an overhead emergency call for a team of experts to intervene and try to save a patient's life when he or she is dying). The MD asked what was hanging in the IV (intravenous therapy) and gave epinephrine and Benadryl for acute anaphylaxis. The child's father at the bedside was panicked, watching his child turn blue and unable to breathe. It turned out the ICU RNs had just hung a new antibiotic in postsurgery ICU recovery, and then I got the patient—right after they'd started the IV drug. I *never* forgot that lesson: always check to see what new drug has just been given (especially in the IV) when a patient "reacts" to something acutely.

A caring, dedicated nurse who takes you under his or her wing can make all the difference in your first job. Bobbi taught me so many other things, but the stories will soon commence.

In Mount Shasta Hospital, a seasoned RN started to teach me how to read EKGs. I'll never forget her, saying, "It's easy: just look at groupings of leads, look at EKG leads two, three, and foot; that's an inferior myocardial infarction." That began my lifelong love for EKG reading and cardiac care.

At Mercy San Juan, multiple people were some of the wonderful RNs who poured their years of experience into my life. I highly recommend anyone in any new job: find someone friendly, caring, and knowledgeable to use as your "go-to person" when you have a question. Dan taught me about Christianity in the workplace and so many deep concepts about ventilators (breathing machines). His big heart and knowledge level were on a different plane.

"Being confident of this, that He who began a good work in you will carry it on to completion until the day of Jesus Christ."

— Philippians 1:6

"As iron sharpens iron, so one man sharpens another."

— Proverbs 27:17

TEACHING MOMENT

Find someone willing to answer your questions and teach you. Stay humble. No question is stupid. Find someone who loves what they do and wants to share. If they grumble about being too busy, stay kind and tell them that you really want to know and learn when they have time.

OUT TO CHANGE
THE WORLD—
THE REALITY
IN THE FIRST YEAR

This was the beginning of the learning curve in a lifelong job. I quickly learned I had to work weekends, holidays, and all hours of the day and night. I was on my feet the entire time for eight hours, rarely sitting or charting (then on paper). I rarely got breaks or dinner. My "dinner" was egg custard from the patient's fridge and some juice at midnight as I sat down to chart after the other shift had come on. I drove right by a Jack in the Box for my 12:30 a.m. "dinner." I realized it was a twenty-four-hour job, and whatever you could not finish, the next shift would take over—where you left off.

My brain stretched immeasurably; I realized I had the kind of job that could hurt or kill someone if I made a mistake. The responsibility was heavy and sobering. One night (on the three to eleven p.m. shift), a drunk MD called me (he was slurring his speech and at a New Year's party) and told me to give a patient one hundred units of insulin for high blood sugar. I was a spanking brand-new RN but knew one hundred units of insulin were way too much to give at once, so I called a mentor. The hospital-charge RN took over, and indeed, it was a wrong order to go and give, so the MD was called back for a more reasonable order. I learned the buck stops here, and you do not always get correct orders from MDs.

The biggest lesson I learned almost got me fired, though it was not my fault. One night, I was in charge on a medical-surgical floor, and one of the patients fell on the floor. The floors were carpet over cement, and she was elderly and fell hard onto her hip and hit her head. She had a "goose egg" on her head and was screaming in pain from her hurting hip. We were unable to move her at all. I knew this was bad and she probably had a head injury, and maybe a broken hip or femur (large thighbone), with bleeding. I immediately called the MD and was told to watch her and that he was busy. After a few more minutes, she was whimpering (instead of screaming), barely conscious, and very pale. I figured she was bleeding from the hip and the head injury was worsening. I called the MD two more times, and he said, "Keep watching her; let me know if she worsens." I tried to tell him she *was* worse. He said he was busy doing taxes and would not listen to me try to explain how bad she looked. I immediately called the house supervisor of the hospital and had her see the patient. She called the MD, and of course, he came right in. As soon as he saw the patient, he started screaming orders to get her to ICU and order blood. He at least had the good sense not to yell at me for not letting him know how sick she was. I had it all documented, as did the house-charge RN. I heard the patient died a few hours later in ICU with a severely broken hip with much bleeding and a bad head injury. I got advice from the house-charge RN and took my documentation to the CEO of the hospital. I showed him my findings and said I was upset with not being able to get the MD to believe me or come in sooner, that maybe the patient would not have died. The MD had a brother and a father, both MDs at this same hospital, and they brought in many patients and much money. I was told that if I pursued this, I would

Debra Bauguess

be "let go." I was in my very first job after only about eight months, and this scared me. I needed to work and could not get fired. It also made me sad and angry, as I learned the world works differently than I'd thought. There actually was a book written for nurses, called *Reality Shock* (by Marlene Kramer), about the things you would see that were different from your idealistic, perfect view of nursing and the way it would be in reality.

I then took a job from one p.m. to nine p.m. for a fellow RN who was having surgery. It was to admit pre-op patients and do their pre-op teaching and preps. I loved it, and that started my love of teaching. I learned that the patients who had all their questions answered before the surgery did much better than those that didn't—what a concept! I "saw, smelled, and heard" so many new and different things. The ability to deal with so much new stuff was overwhelming at times.

This actually never changed for forty-two years. Even in my last year of nursing, the changes and new things were constantly happening. It's the kind of job where you have to be on your A game for the entire time you are there. A patient's life depends on it. I loved surgical patients and did not like medical patients at first when I worked those floors; though I came to respect the patients and nurses in each area I worked, that wasn't my "home station." I hated ICU at first, too, but ended up there for the rest of my life. You can never predict what you will stay in. You really have to have an open mind about change and know you will continue to find new things that you will like.

I got married to my college boyfriend and had a honeymoon in Tahiti. We then soon moved out of the area. I found out so many new concepts and ways to treat people and ways to change myself to be a better person that first year. The learning curve was just starting to go up, though. I believe it never stopped going up.

"In their hearts humans plan their course, but the Lord establishes their steps."

— Proverbs 16:9

"Many are the plans in a person's heart, but it is the Lord's purpose that prevails."

— Proverbs 19:21

TEACHING MOMENT

Reality and life are different from textbooks. Be open to change and learn new things. Don't expect real life to be perfect. There are times that dash your expectations and times that exceed them; learn from both. Stay true to who you are and your values as a person advocating for the patient.

Debra Bauguess

BECOMING HUMBLE

On my first day on the job (in 1978), I felt lost and, oh, so inadequate. I had all this book knowledge and not a lot of actual hands-on experience. I noticed there were only two RNs, one orderly, one LVN (licensed vocational nurse), and an aide for about fifty patients on two hallways. I had no assumptions of delineations in job descriptions. I saw that everyone was working hard and giving their all. I learned fast that if you expect to be helped, you need to help others. I can actually say I learned the "golden rule" in my first week.

Here I was with a fancy bachelor's degree, twenty-three years old and straight out of school, with basically no experience. The orderly, LVN, and aide had been working for a very long time, and the two RNs were well senior in experience. I was scared and wanted to do everything right as far as giving and getting respect from people more used to the job, which was so new to me. All the workers were at least ten to forty years older than me. I found out that no job was too menial. If a sixty-year-old aide could clean up patients' accidents, then I could too. I also learned that a call light gets answered by anyone walking by it; you never say, "It's not my patient." Forty years later, I've been in a hospital where the call light of my mom was on, and she desperately needed help, and several people just walked by. When I answered anyone's light and did any job, I earned respect and got help when I needed it. This was the first *big* lesson I learned.

I believe most of the workers there probably had a preconceived notion of what a young bachelor's degree RN would act like, and I did not want to prove them right. You need to realize that, in any job, I would not ask someone else to do something I would not do. I know this sounds magnanimous and like I'm some saint, but, truthfully, I believe the Lord helped show me. I "saw" the need to learn these ideas immediately and followed through and earned love, friendship, and undying respect from all who originally thought I "was above it all." When you humble yourself and play the servant's role, you place that person (whether nurse or patient) first, before yourself.

Everyone has worth. Every role is important. I'll talk later about the importance of the team. It's never one person that saves a life; it's multiple people: from housekeepers to lab, to an EKG tech, to a nurse, to a social worker, to an MD. It's so very important to realize you are in a group that works together like a well-oiled machine. Respect and friendship are not something you can pay for or expect if you don't put your own effort and time into it. When you treat others the way you want to be treated, it pretty much covers all bases. It should be this way in any job, not just nursing: when you do your best with your knowledge, strength, and words (which includes saying "thank you" to all others who help you), you honor them for who they are. Your own heart and the humility of the servant's role teach you. It is not something you can teach someone else. This lays the groundwork for a long career based on giving love to receive the joy that keeps you going.

One a.m., as I got a report on my patient, I saw a housekeeper struggling with a room a patient had just left. Admittedly, the patient had left in a hurry to transfer out at shift change, and we had to do a report, but the room was a mess. I learned early on, in ICU, that you clean up your room, empty all body fluids in appropriate containers, and strip the patient's dirty, soiled linens, tubings, and pumps of any kind. The housekeeper should not ever have to touch any soiled or contaminated object that you can first get rid of. They are not allowed to touch meds (hanging IV drips still in the room) either. The faster you "strip your room," the faster it gets cleaned safely, and the faster it's ready for any new admit. You then stock the room for anything you might need for a sudden admit; this is nursing 101. The housekeeper came out and gently said she wasn't sure what to do with some of the things we usually had cleaned up before they got there. The room looked like a tornado had hit it. I know the outgoing RN wanted to go home and give a report, but the housekeeper had been left in a compromising situation. The other RN then said, "Let her do it; it's her job." I was dismayed because the housekeeper heard her. I got up from the report and quickly stripped the things in the room that the other RN should have. I then sat down to finish my report. I think the RN was a little upset with me, but I'd earned the undying respect from that one housekeeper forever.

I think actions speak louder than words, and hopefully, any "servant" role done in love will speak out for itself to any who are watching you. It's actually a very simple concept: treat others the way you want to be treated.

> *Therefore, as God's chosen people, holy and dearly loved, clothe yourselves with compassion, kindness, humility, gentleness and patience. Bear with each other and forgive one another if any of you has a grievance against someone. Forgive as the Lord forgave you.*

And over all these virtues put on love, which binds them all together in perfect unity.

— Colossians 3:12–14

"Wisdom's instruction is to fear the LORD, and humility comes before honor."

— Proverbs 15:33

TEACHING MOMENT

Take "self" out of your situation. You have chosen a job of being a servant. Stay open and *see* from the viewpoints of others. Know that the more you learn about what the patient needs, the more you improve yourself.

Debra Bauguess

EXPECTATIONS

PATIENT'S EXPECTATIONS

This human being lying in the hospital bed is away from all they know and are comfortable with. Their normal routine and life, as they knew it, have abruptly changed. They are away from family (during COVID-19 right now) and may be in pain, fearful of an unknown future, angry, grieving, frustrated, anxious, worried, in denial, or depressed. They have a *deep* need for you to be there for them and help them in their time of need. They have lost control over the circumstances and their lives.

They also may feel you "owe" them or they are in a five-star hotel and should be treated like a VIP. Many come with a chip on their shoulder: they expect to be cared for, cured, or fixed, given hope, pain taken away, and given answers.

They rightfully deserve kindness, openness, truth, honesty, and help with what's next. "What's next" could be recovery, further nursing care in an acute or chronic phase, or financial help. We, as their caregivers, *need* to be their advocate and liaison between them, the MDs, and all other departments. The patient wants you to understand them, *listen* to them, care about their side of the story, and, just maybe, hold their hand.

Carl W. Buehner once said, "It's not what you say or what you do; it's how you make them feel that they remember." They need *love*, but each person has a different life story and a journey they are on, and none should be treated the same. There are so many dysfunctional families in our world today that one person's needs are tightly wound with the needs of multiple other family members and friends.

FAMILY EXPECTATIONS

Most of all, they want their loved one helped. You learn in the first year of work that the patient is not the only one you are treating or caring for. The MDs may treat and write orders for the patient only, but the nurse and all other departments also include the family. They deserve to be listened to and cared about.

So much of what is done in a hospital is overwhelmingly foreign to nonmedically grounded people. They need to be taught and have *everything* explained to them in honesty and truthfulness. They want the RN to be the go-between for their concerns and the MD's explanations. The RN is stuck in a hard place, defending their unit and practice standards, their MDs, and the patient/family's wishes and concerns. The golden rule applies in this job (as it should in all things in life), and we should treat the patient and family as we would want to be treated ourselves. They desire to be understood even if they have a different culture or language.

Many times, a family demands crowd control and for the RN to police all people who visit. I've been told to keep the ex-wife and current girlfriend (or current wife) apart, certain family members and friends out (including the patient not wanting the immediate family in the room at all), and any number of combination of others out (or at least not in the room at the same time). It gets very confusing, and our desk clerk used to keep lists of people that "could" and "could not" visit. It really was too much to deal with when you were desperately trying to keep the patient alive. I had the patient's "stalker" walk in on me once, as we didn't have locked doors to our unit.

The family usually wants their loved one to be treated in a special way and can get very demanding for every little thing (when they could do some of it, like wipe a face) when you have another patient to take care of also. They expect nothing bad to happen and for the patient to only get better. Since I spent forty-one of my forty-two years in critical care, I know it's hard to explain to a family member how "critical" their loved one is and give hope at the same time, all the while knowing we do not have *all* the answers to who lives and who doesn't. The family expects perfection and zero mistakes, though we are all human and can only do our very best with what we are trained to do. One of the hardest things to deal with is when multiple family members expect to be called for *any* reason, like *any* change in condition (good or bad) or *any* lab result. We become experts at explaining that our time is better spent at the bedside of their loved one than on the phone with ten different siblings, giving each the same information. It is very important to have *one* spokesperson for every family, who can be the *only* one we update. That one person can then make the multiple calls to all other family members. The patient is not isolated; they are a part of a group, even if it's friends (they have no family) or a conservator or caregiver. They *all* are part of who we are caring for in every single situation, even though the patient in the bed is getting the hands-on meds and treatment.

MD'S EXPECTATIONS

A doctor expects the patient and/or family to listen, understand, and ask appropriate questions. They want trust from the patient and family and for the "spokesperson" to be available at all times for any emergency need. When someone's life is in our hands, the need to have them understand we are doing everything humanly possible for them is paramount. MDs expect the RN to be fast, efficient, and never make a mistake. They want us to listen and obey and know our patient/family's needs, as well as the disease process in each patient's case and all procedures that our specific unit would perform.

They deserve respect and to be treated kindly, even if they are tired or snapping at you. We all get moments of tiredness or stress, and we should never take it out on each other or the patients or family. It takes time, usually years, to develop a rapport or mutual peer respect between an RN and the intensive care MD they frequently work with. Trust is given after much time spent together in stressful, critical situations where the MD and RN work, side by side, with the same goal: to save a life. Once the mutual like, trust, and respect are given both directions between the RN and MD, there is nothing like it. There are some cardiologists and pulmonologists I worked with for many, many years (some over thirty years), and the mutual respect and trust turned to friendship, which brought joy to my career.

WORKPLACE EXPECTATIONS
(HOSPITAL, OFFICE, ETC.)

The place of employment expects loyalty and hard, honest work with a good attitude. Nursing involves feelings of patients and

Debra Bauguess

families, so hospitals are constantly trying to improve things like patient satisfaction. I feel patient safety should be paramount. They expect you to be a steward of resources. We all know the dollar is the bottom line in keeping any workplace solvent and open. Employers expect longevity, knowledge, human kindness, and true caring for *all* people, each color and race. They want you to adhere to their rules and standards and do all the (constant and frequent) mandatory education items your institution and license require. Mainly, we keep up with privacy laws and state requirements (like adult and child protective service reporting). Unfortunately, today, there are many classes needed on trafficking and violence.

The place of employment will want you to reflect well on them and "sell" them to the public. They want their hospital to be the one all your friends would choose for the excellent care.

MY EXPECTATIONS

I wanted to be employed by someone who valued me as a worker and a person. I wanted security with enough of a paycheck to pay bills and be able to live life comfortably. I needed health insurance and wanted a pension. I wanted MDs, peers, and hospital administrators to be approachable and kind and my work environment to be safe. I expected the proper on-the-job training, respect, and hopefully, shift work hours I could live with. I needed full-time work. I also wanted my place of employment to stand up for me, legally, if I was in the right and a patient, family, or MD unrighteously attacked me. I ultimately wanted a job I could grow old with and find happiness in and fulfillment with.

It ended up becoming my "mission field" and was a way to serve God by loving His created people. It brought me great joy and was my passion—*never just a job*. The fruit of my hard work was, is from, and was through God. I was responsible for the emotional, spiritual, and physical well-being of all those under my care. I know I would become dissatisfied if I lost the sense of purpose God intended for me and gave me. As a single woman, I also needed a job I could always turn to that would support me if I ever found myself alone in life at some point (which I was, for most of my life).

> *"Whatever your hand finds to do, do it with all your might."*
>
> — Ecclesiastes 9:10

TEACHING MOMENT

Don't expect too much from anyone, including yourself. Be true to yourself. Your needs should come last and are still important, but you are choosing this profession to help others. Be respectful of leadership; their job is harder than you know (I know this firsthand). Your job is to be the patient's advocate but support your employer. Join committees if you want a change.

Debra Bauguess

FIRST IMPRESSIONS

I believe God gives us assignments and rewards. Stripped of God's love, our service is futile. I used to pray in my car, in the parking garage, every morning before work. I'd ask God to place me in an assignment He specifically needed me in and to let others see His love through me. I'd ask for the physical, mental, and emotional ability to get through the twelve-hour shift (as I aged, my arthritis made it very difficult for me to lift and be on my feet).

I'd ask for Him to show me which patients needed me. At the beginning of a shift or patient assignment, you start to judge and formulate an opinion as soon as you hear a report from the previous nurse. You may even hear comments from fellow staff, upon entering the unit, about a certain patient or family that are difficult. You may walk by a room and see a patient screaming, being abusive, falling out of bed, or urinating on the floor, and you secretly hope you don't get that assignment. It's only human to want a good shift with minimal problems. Rule number one in ICU is: things that are unexpected emergently happen at a moment's notice. It's the nature of "intensive" in ICU.

First, you get an assignment and immediately formulate a quick summary of what your day might become based on what you saw or heard upon arrival and then based on your one-to-one report. You feel challenged, excited, moved emotionally, or overwhelmed before you even walk through the doorway. I learned to pray for God to give me the right words before

I walked through a patient's doorway to meet the patient for the first time. I learned the shift went better if I immediately showed caring, concern, and friendliness in the first few seconds. I started by saying, "I will do my very best for you today." I needed to immediately squelch feelings of dislike, dismay, or fear upon first meeting the patient. Sometimes they would be writhing on the bed in restraints (for their own safety), reaching for life-supporting lines and tubes. Mostly, they were pleasant and grateful right back to you. When you saw a room in disarray and a patient half off the bed, lying in a mess, your heart would sink, knowing you were starting off behind schedule. Many times the patient was comatose (asleep due to brain injury or being very critically ill), and you immediately met a distraught family member wanting to vent the last four days' worth of their frustrations to you, all in the first ten minutes of meeting you.

You learn to accept what you see, feel, and hear and immediately ask God for help and step into your day. Work, accepted as an assignment from God, can be seen as a teaching moment or a gift. There were days where the good beginning got much worse and where the crazy beginning became "a piece of cake." Some days you had a to-do list an entire page long, were two steps behind all day, and *ran* as fast as you could for twelve and a half hours. I often forsook breaks, water, coffee, bathroom stops, or lunch because the patient came first and the emergent care was nonstop. On those days, you invariably ran into some overtime and got home after driving in a stupor. I would sit still in my uniform in front of a TV with something inane on for distraction and realize I had had one cup of coffee, one cup of water, and a few bites of a brief lunch and never used the bathroom. You would be completely numb and unable to make

Debra Bauguess

the simplest decision, like: Should I change or eat or shower first?

On the good days, you came home undrained and sometimes felt overjoyed over an assignment from God that left you knowing He used you in a specific situation for that patient that shift. The challenge became: What do I make of this assignment today, and how do I figure out (like a detective) what this patient or family needs and wants in the twelve hours? It never failed to amaze me how a patient's attitude or my attitude would change with time and effort. It truly was rare that I left feeling frustrated, helpless, or angry. There was always *good* that had been done, and I would know I had done everything in my power to help this patient or family, whether they appreciated it or not. All we can do is our best.

My first impressions of the patient and myself often changed by the shift's end. You cannot judge an assignment or patient or family in seconds or minutes. It takes patience, deep caring, and love for a suffering person and time to turn around the initial impression. Because of my praying in my car, there were days I was completely awed at how the needs of the patient or family were met by a strength, experience, or specific knowledge I had. Even the hardest of assignments with uncooperative patients would end up changing me after twelve hours. I always left feeling humbled and blessed. My life's problems were never as much of an issue after I saw twenty ICU families and patients with such dire needs. (Our neuro ICU had twenty beds.)

The grumpiest people would start to respond favorably to you, eventually, if you kept taking *time* to talk to them, share a piece of your life, and then listen to whatever they had to say. They always had something to say when they knew you cared and were interested in them. Even the most difficult patient (usually in withdrawal from drugs or alcohol or mentally ill) was worthy of my sorrow for their plight, and I could still show *love* to them and the overwrought family. I often came home and prayed for them or cried. I would maybe see an abused-animal commercial, and it would cause me to start sobbing. I realized it was God's way of helping me decompress what I'd seen and felt all day. No matter how impossible the day may look, never give in to fear or despair; just know you are human and can only move one step at a time and do one thing well at a time. You will get through the shift, and the next shift coming in to take over will relieve you of your duties. It's a twenty-four-hour job, and whatever you, in good conscience, cannot finish, the next shift will. Most of the time, the next shift was grateful for what I'd done and gracious to continue what still needed doing. I learned to be that way to the nurse leaving when I started because I wanted them to treat me the same way at my shift's end.

Patients are not intentionally trying to ruin your day; they are in pain, scared, and their lives are in chaos. They and their families have lost control of their lives. You have a choice to love them and help give them relief and control back where possible. The bottom line is you are there as a patient and family's advocate in a position of power. It often deals with life and death. You owe it to the patient, yourself, and the hospital (or place of employment) to do your best with what knowledge you have to uplift, comfort, and provide safety for the loved one in your hands.

"For we are God's handiwork, created in Christ Jesus to do good works, which God prepared in advance for us to do."

— Ephesians 2:10

"Commit to the Lord whatever you do, and he will establish your plans."

— Proverbs 16:3

TEACHING MOMENT

Never let first impressions throw you off. The most grim-looking day can turn into a life-changing moment for the better. Stay open-minded and step into every situation with a seeking heart. Not all *is* as it *seems* at first. Do a lot of deep breathing and counting to ten before entering a room with a challenging patient or if you have difficult news to impart.

THE GOLDEN RULE AND SETTING BOUNDARIES

These are actually concepts it took me years to understand, but they are so necessary to be taught to students and caregivers up front. In my first year, I took care of a young man with a brain abscess from snorting cocaine (he'd had brain surgery for it). He was "on his light" every half hour for more pain meds. He was about seventeen years old and had several friends, all the same age, in his room. They would laugh at me and make many rude and crude comments (today called sexual harassment). I felt a little scared—my first few months on the job, just out of school—intimidated, and inadequately trained to deal with this. I was not an assertive person yet. My mentor said to go right back in and tell them how their comments made me feel. She insisted that I should say that I deserved respect and to be treated as I was treating him. I cared about him, and I was the one bringing the pain meds and treatments he needed. If they wanted to have me continue to care for him, they should be respectful with their words. If they did not want me caring for their friend, then I would get someone else. They actually all were apologetic and sorry they had offended me and wanted to have me keep caring for him because I was nice to him and cared about him. I felt this huge weight lift off my shoulders: I had just learned to set a boundary and earn respect. Those boys were good to me the next few weeks that I took care of their friend; I never had another issue.

Years later, I took care of an African-American woman who had a large CVA (stroke); she had been in our unit for about a week, and I had cared for her several days in a row. We had a family meeting with multiple family members to discuss her prognosis and condition and answer questions. The nature of ICU is that so much time is required to care for the patients that the MD, who is rounding on multiple patients and covering numerous procedures and emergencies, cannot just drop everything and talk to every family member who comes in or calls. We had to set special times for a half hour or more from two p.m. to four p.m. every day to do family meetings.

The MD and I faced a room with about eight people in it, some immediate family (children, grandchildren, or siblings) and a few who had never seen her and had flown or driven in to see her for the first time. Over half the people there did not have a good understanding of how ill she was or how poor her prognosis was. They came in angry and with a definite "chip on their shoulder." They were already determined to blame anything said that wasn't good on us. The MD and I explained her state and said how very sorry we were but that everything humanly possible was being done, and she was not getting better. This was the case, sadly, with many of our stroke patients. It's such a devastating condition much of the time.

When we asked if they had any questions, they immediately jumped on us and started verbally attacking the MD and me. They "pulled the race card" and accused us of treating her differently because of her skin color. The ones accusing us of this had not called or come in to see her the entire time she had been there and were suddenly here, accusing the people, who were trying the hardest to help her, of racism. I have to admit I was angry. I did not show it or say anything retaliatory but did say that I had *never* in my forty years of nursing treated *anyone* differently due to race or color. Of course, they could not hear it and remained angry and accusatory, saying *we* had caused her problem and were responsible for her not getting better.

It's so frustrating to have some stranger come in and tell us, a highly educated RN and MD, that *we* are responsible for this lady's high blood pressure, high-salt diet, diabetes, and family history and that *we* only sat and watched her get worse, without laying our hands on her to care for her. I guess that's why my back, shoulders, neck, knees, and hips hurt so badly today: it's all the lifting and care I supposedly did not do. This family yelled at us for over one hour. I learned, *never again*. I have respect for myself and the MD and the care we had been giving this unfortunate woman. We set boundaries, and never again would I let a family accuse me unjustly or yell at me with unfounded anger for that long. I would draw the line at twenty minutes or so and then tell the family that I hoped we had answered all their questions and that I had to go and take care of their loved one now and that we would do our very best for her. Ninety-nine percent of our family meetings were good and informative and helpful and appreciated by all the people who showed up. We were open and honest and always tried to convey caring for all of them and promised to keep them informed.

You must respect yourself and your hard work enough to reflect that to those in your care and your peer group. Peers need to know if you feel disrespected or shamed by them as well. No one has the right to be rude to you—patient, peer, MD, or any other coworker. The golden rule is that you treat others the way you wish to be treated. You can tactfully tell someone you promise to treat them with respect, so you expect the same, please. You have the right to tell anyone gently (try to keep hurt and emotion out of it) that they were rude, unkind or hurt you and to please stop. Walk away if you must, compose yourself and come back with gentleness. When people know who you are and see, over time, you are true to your word in how you treat them, hopefully, they will slowly come to treat you with the same respect.

There is *no excuse* for unkindness or rudeness to any patient or family member. They are in a foreign, scary place with a loss of control over their lives, mental, physical, and emotional needs. They are dealing with pain and life-and-death decisions. Even if they are unkind or rude to you, do not return tit for tat. Kind words or gestures eventually disarm them. Your caring attitude means everything. If they remember a nurse that made them feel cared for, loved, safe, and like everything possible was done for them, then you fulfilled your purpose. You can only pray you are treated the same way if you are in their shoes.

You must set boundaries and "call out" mean words, whether from a peer or a patient. You can legally, morally tell a rude patient that you will give them good care whether they speak unkindly or not but that you deserve and expect respect from them to do your best job. We are *all* worthy of unconditional love and care with kindness. You get what you give. Kindness begets kindness. Everything that is worthwhile takes effort. It's important to know you will not make everyone happy, but trying to show them you care is worth it to you as a human being. It takes much courage to be open with love and not get it back. It builds up your strength to "love anyway." Everyone deserves it whether they know it or not.

Debra Bauguess

If you find yourself saying something snarky or unkind or clipped to a patient or peer, *learn* to apologize quickly. It takes guts and a few seconds to be sorry for your actions. It makes you a better person and nurse. I have to say God gave me the strength to be someone I didn't feel like being at times, especially when I was tired, hungry, in pain, stressed, or worried. The trick is to act quickly and make it be from your heart. Very few people can resist a heartfelt apology. I realized the need (for me) to ask for supernatural strength when faced with a difficult situation, and I would always receive it. Kindness and using the golden rule never returns void; your caregiving career can only benefit from it, as well as you.

> *"Love your neighbor as yourself."*
>
> — Matthew 22:39

> *"The wise in heart are called discerning, and gracious words promote instruction."*
>
> — Proverbs 16:21

TEACHING MOMENT

The most precious gift you can give is yourself! Listen and care—that's all any patient wants. If you treat everyone you encounter as you wish to be treated, you will *never* go wrong. Take time to squelch your initial emotional retorts, take a deep breath, and speak in gentleness to *all* you deal with, no matter how they treat you. Set healthy boundaries when another's anger or frustrations are taken out on you. Just limit your time for them to vent and tell them you need to be at their loved one's side to do your best for all concerned.

PATIENCE

How do you learn to have patience? I believe it comes from God. It usually involves being in a situation that requires you to need patience. I tend to learn things the hard way. If you are not patient when you should be, you tend to hurt mostly yourself and how you project your loving care to a hurting patient. Even if you are so busy with literal life-and-death details that you can hardly keep your thoughts straight, you *can* take a minute to tell a distraught family member that you care.

Many times I had a patient "trying to die" on me, and I was struggling to do six things at once to keep him or her alive. All it takes is one anxious family member to distract you, and you could make a mistake. I've had to go to the spouse (seeing their loved one in the ICU for the first time), take their hands, and say respectfully but honestly that their loved one is critical and that I'm desperately needing to focus on what I'm doing for some time in order to try to save their loved one's life. I then say, "I care about you and the patient, and I promise to do my very best. I will give you details and answer questions once stability is achieved." I usually hug them tight and then tell them where to wait, and I turn my attention back to the patient.

The most trying situations, which make you dig deep for patience, are the most character building. You come through stronger each time, knowing you've given it everything you have. There actually are patients who think they are in a five-star hotel and/or that you are their personal maid. Many people in today's world feel entitled and that this government and country "owe them." It takes a special kind of patience with these needy people. There are the ones who are "on their call light" every five minutes, too. All I can say is: take a deep breath and keep on caring for them to the best of your ability. Words don't show as much as actions. You can debate with an anxious patient on the light all day, but make the time you are in the room mean something. Do whatever it takes to make that person feel special and cared for and give them a brief reason for leaving, like, "I need to answer my other patient's light," and then tell them when you will be back. The "entitled" ones or the ones ordering you to fetch new ice every time you walk by take an extra ounce of patience and lots of deep breaths on your part. Thank God, 90 percent or more are very grateful for any care. A simple explanation helps, or at least, sticking to your own word and showing up when you said you would goes a long way.

If and when you lose your patience: apologize quickly and mean it. We are *all* human. I've apologized many times and had patients apologize to me after becoming impatient with me not "doing enough" or "moving fast enough." I've just told them I can only do one thing at a time but can do it well.

There was an MD who would ask me to do four things at once. I would tell him, "I only have two hands and can only do one thing at a time. What would you like me to do *first*?" I also told him, "You drive me crazy," and he would always say, "Do you have far to go?" We are friends, as well as peers, to this day. I used to get so frustrated with his always being in a rush, and now I deeply admire him and believe he has the same amount of respect and caring for me. I've often asked myself why patience is so much easier with total strangers than with your own family. I suppose it's because you see an end in sight with the stranger: your shift ends in twelve hours. The family also know how to push your buttons. Even strangers can do that, not knowing you, but when you know you will never see them again, it's easier to be extra patient.

When you feel pushed beyond your limit, take a deep, cleansing breath. I used to whisper a quick prayer for wisdom, strength, and the right words before walking back into their room. Just keep moving forward at a steady, safe speed, knowing *this, too, shall pass*. The situation and shift will end, and you will eventually leave, knowing you did your best. Patience is not something you can teach any new nurse or caregiver, it takes time and probably several mistakes, but most of us *do* learn. It makes your life and the patient's life go easier.

"Be completely humble and gentle; be patient, bearing with one another in love."

— Ephesians 4:2

"A hot-tempered person stirs up conflict, but the one who is patient calms a quarrel."

— Proverbs 15:18

TEACHING MOMENT

Patience takes time to perfect. Take a deep breath, count to ten, and let the other person speak first. Address their issues and then calmly state yours. In time, you learn to control some or most of your initial emotional reactions, and then you become more effective in what you have to say. Be aware of the things that affect your patience level: lack of sleep, lack of food (low blood sugar), too much to do and not enough help, dehydration (drink your water), and any perceived slight from another stressed person.

WHEN YOU CANNOT
GET THROUGH

In this life, it's important to know you will not make everyone you meet happy. There are many reasons you have no control over. I can honestly say there were very few patients that were not happy with me. I took it as a personal challenge and taught this to my students: to try and reach or get through to the patient or family by the end of the shift by sharing part of yourself. It's called investing. You get what you give. Everyone has worth. When you've tried with all you have, and it doesn't work, you still did the right thing. The ones who don't reflect or respond to your kindness are usually on drugs, in drug withdrawal, or having a psychotic mental break due to mental illness.

I've learned not to feel defeated when I cannot get through to someone. Drugs, withdrawal, mental illness, or brain damage affect the brain to where a patient physically cannot respond to anyone in a meaningful way. You just do the best you know how to do and keep them safe and let the family know you care.

Safety is usually an issue in each of these instances. You must have your own boundaries and stay safe from kicking, scratching, spitting, hitting, biting, and verbal abuse. It *will* happen many times in an ICU career. You must not ever blame the patient or take it personally; they are not in their right mind and are incapable of normal response. I once had a woman who had fallen down some stairs, hit her head, and had a frontal-lobe (front part of your brain) contusion.

Frontal-lobe injuries affect your acting out. The injured have no filters or inhibition. They may curse like a sailor, scream and yell out, hit, kick, bite, and scratch or spit. She was in four-point restraints (wrists and ankles) just to attempt to keep her in the bed and from kicking and hitting. She managed to scream at the top of her lungs every foul word and rude derogatory term she knew, aiming them at me and the MD and anyone else who walked by. I had to shut her glass door and watch through the window. She was extremely agitated, trying to throw her body off the bed the entire shift. I couldn't get any nurses to help me reposition her in bed, as she squirmed off repeatedly, because they were scared of getting scratched or hit. The MD could not give me any sedation, as it was a brain injury with swelling, and we cannot sedate to avoid masking neuro signs. Every time I got near her, she kicked and scratched me. I actually filed a violence report and went home with scratches and bruises.

Those shifts I will never miss. You just survive them and do your best. Two days later, she was walking down the hallway, completely normal. She was sweet and apologetic, not even remembering me. The swelling had gone down enough to let her frontal lobe regain control of her inhibitions.

After I had my second knee surgery for arthritis damage, I returned to work, having three months off to recover beforehand. My first patient was in alcohol and methamphetamine withdrawal, in restraints, screaming and hitting. He had a very worried mom at the bedside. She demanded I remove his wrist restraints because we were hurting him.

When we "restrain" patients, it's with soft, easily releasable ties that are for the patient's safety. It keeps them from falling out of bed and fracturing something and keeps their life support hooked up to them, like IVs and central lines and breathing tubes.

Another nurse and I decided to at least try it. As soon as we released his arms, he tried to hit me, and I put up my two arms to block his punch. My charge RN saw it and came to help me rerestrain the patient. The mom started getting upset with me and went right to my manager to complain that I was "abusing" her son. I knew she was unreasonable and upset and that it was probably stress and worry at seeing her son in this condition (withdrawal). I tried extra hard to be kind and help her, knowing she loved this boy in the bed, no matter what he was acting like. She did not want me anywhere near her son again for the rest of the shift, even though I had two RN witnesses who saw him take a swing at me.

I got a talking-to by my manager, though he heard the truth from others. I was sixty-four years old, after my second knee surgery, and it was my first day back in a profession I'm supposed to love. I knew it was not my fault and there were many issues with the mom and her son, both being extremely dysfunctional. I went to a women's Bible study the next morning and said I didn't think I could be a nurse anymore and described the situation (no HIPAA violation, just generalities). I started sobbing and was ready to end my nursing career. About eight ladies came to me, and there were about ten others in the room. They were laying hands on me and praying for me to have strength and hope and be restored.

I know to this day the faith and prayers of godly women (in my desperate moment) helped me work another year and a half to retirement. An ICU nurse *will* face many difficult situations like this. It's not personal, and it's the strength you find to keep going back to the job day after day, which gets you through. With me, it was my faith and prayers from caring friends.

I must say my fourteen or so years in neuro critical care were the most physically challenging I've *ever* had. Much of it was spent wrestling with patients and fighting battles you will never win when someone with a brain injury cannot act nice or normal. You still *give it your all.* There is no excuse for failing to give care and love to someone needing it, whether you can "reach" them or not. Every day is different; you keep your faith, have hope for a better day with your next shift, and count each lesson learned as character building.

> *"A gentle answer turns away wrath, but a harsh word stirs up anger."*
>
> — Proverbs 15:1

> *"A happy heart makes the face cheerful, but heartache crushes the spirit."*
>
> — Proverbs 15:13

TEACHING MOMENT

We cannot fix everyone, but we can choose to care about all of them. Treat them with dignity despite their choices, faults, or actions. God sees us all with the same love. Develop a thick skin; their words cannot hurt you if you are doing your best.

Debra Bauguess

MAKING A
DIFFERENCE—
THE POWER OF LOVE

You get friendships that miracles and tragedy forged in moments of fear, pain, life, and death. Forever, you hold in your heart each face and moment in time when you changed someone's life and made them feel, just for one moment, that you loved them unconditionally. You love the addicted patients, peers, and MDs because not one of us is perfect. You shine your light given by God to make a difference in this world.

I believe, and for me, to love everyone and make a difference, you have to be "called" and know who you are in God. I feel the Lord selected me to be a caregiver before the beginning of time. He knew my gifts, strengths, and failings. I became a messenger to show love, grace, mercy, and care. I became the hands and feet of the Lord to reflect His heart. I became a conduit to be used to minister to those who have a desperate need.

To be a caregiver is to *want* to serve. It's not about *you*. Rawsi Williams said, "To do what nobody else will do, in a way that nobody else can do, in spite of all we go through; that is to be a nurse." First Peter 3:8 says, "Finally, all of you, be like-minded, be sympathetic, love one another, be compassionate and humble." My prayer always was, "Lord, You understand every hurt and need. I ask You to give me the eyes and mind of Christ as I seek to serve others in Your name."

No act of kindness, no matter how small, is ever wasted. Comfort is in the small things. To be a better comforter to those in pain, put yourself in the other person's place, do not give pat answers or say, "I know how you feel," offer help and encouragement, love and understand them, do not analyze or give advice; the best comforters *know* something about suffering.

To make a difference and love people, you need to be able to comfort, show empathy, and have compassion. In my first years in nursing, I learned that small things bring comfort. Every time I assisted with a patient procedure, where they were awake with a sterile drape covering their face, I slipped my gloved hand under the drape and held their hand. I knew they were having pain and were scared, and I asked myself what I'd want. My hand used to get almost crushed, as they would latch on with a superhuman strength, in their fear. I would also speak to them soothingly and encourage them.

After holding a German-speaking patient's hand, I started to clean up. He kept trying to lick his lips with a dry tongue, so I got a clean wet washcloth and wet his lips and wiped his face. As I turned to leave, he grabbed my hand and said, "On... gel, on...gel." I finally understood that he was saying "angel." That spurred me on to always comfort by touch where I could.

Once, I was in the emergency room early in the morning. I had awakened to a swelling throat and had difficulty swallowing. I knew it was an allergic reaction and went in. I basically sat in the ER for three hours, waiting for the antihistamine and steroids to work. I was freezing, alone in a room with no sign of anyone, for almost two hours. A housekeeper went by, and I asked for help and said I was cold. She went and got two warm blankets out of a warmer for me. I felt cared for and not

Debra Bauguess

"lost in the system" for a while and blessedly warm. I will *never* forget her. I used to thank her and hug her every time I saw her after that.

You cannot teach someone to have empathy, compassion or give comfort. It's innate and/or a gift. Once you encounter it, you are changed and led to be the same way to *all* those you come across, whether in the hospital or not. To truly love, you need an open heart that accepts everyone: every color, every race, every age, and every emotionally distraught, physically hurting human being placed in your path. There is no judgment because I will be judged one day myself. Again, you treat others the way you want to be treated, and you will never go wrong. You do invest a piece of your soul with empathy because, for a time, you feel what they are going through, and your heart hurts with them. I would touch, hug, encourage, cry with, and pray with them, then go home and cry. You've had the privilege to share in someone else's pain to hopefully lighten their load by knowing someone is there who cares.

> *"In the same way, let your light shine before others, that they may see your good deeds and praise your Father in heaven."*
>
> — Matthew 5:16

> *"Anxiety weighs down the heart, but a kind word cheers it up."*
>
> — Proverbs 12:25

TEACHING MOMENT

You need to show empathy, compassion, and care in the small things: a touch, smile, direct eye contact, tears, the words "I care," and meaningful gestures like a glass of water or pulling up a blanket. It takes time and effort to *do* something extra and small for someone (patient or family member), but it will never return void to you.

Debra Bauguess

CARING: THE JOY AND THE PAIN

God gave me a caring heart because I asked Him to, and I was made to be an emotional person. I feel things very deeply. I tear up at any moving moment, whether joy, tenderness, or sorrow. I used to think I was unusually and overly emotional, but now I know I'm just the way the Lord made me to be. Many people do not cry or feel as deeply as I do in everyday things. Many do not even like touching (especially after COVID-19), but I realized I have a unique gift to convey care when people need it most. I prayed to God to break my heart for what breaks His. He has opened the "eyes" of my soul and done what I asked for. I feel more sorrow and pain this way but can cry it out at home.

When you feel and share in someone else's pain, they know it and *feel* you have a personal stake in their life. Often, I would immediately tear up at a patient's bad news, miracle, or something touching. I think my favorite touching moment happened at my first CCU (coronary care unit) job in Sacramento. My patient was dying from congestive heart failure (the lungs fill up with fluid, as the heart does not pump well anymore). He was a DNR (do-not-resuscitate order). He was literally drowning in lung fluids with clammy, ice-cold skin and was gasping. We gave comfort with meds per his wishes. His real wife and daughter did not want to deal with his dying or touch his clammy hands and waited outside our unit in a waiting room until he was "gone." I had a hard time dealing with their seeming lack of love for him.

His stepdaughter sat by his bed, holding his cold, wet hands, and stroked his icy forehead. She kept saying over and over, "I love you." His gasping slowed, and his heart and breathing stopped, and I told her he had passed, and I was so very sorry. She started crying and said, "I wish I could have told him one more time that I loved him." I quietly started unhooking things and picking up the room, and about a full minute went by as she wept and held his hand. Suddenly, he opened his eyes, took a deep breath, looked right at her, and said, "I know," and then closed his eyes a final time. She and I looked at one another, and both hugged and cried together. It was such an absolutely beautiful and tender moment in time. She would be assured, forever, that he did *know* how much she loved him. His love for her transcended death. We said good-bye to each other, knowing we had witnessed a miracle defying explanation, which was a gift from above to us both. Each one of these glimpses into unconditional love changes us forever.

I had a sweet little older man with some sort of internal bleeding that they were trying to find the source of with multiple tests. I fell in love with him and his wife in one shift and went home, praying they'd be able to help him. I couldn't wait to see him again the next morning. The next day, I walked into the CCU and headed directly to his room to say good morning and that I'd missed him. A fellow RN grabbed me and pulled me back. I said, "I want to say hello to him," and she said, "Debbie, you can't; he just died. We just finished CPR on him." I literally burst into tears as she held me. She knew me and knew how deeply I cared and wanted to spare me the shock of walking in on his body. I will never forget him or my friend, DJ. The man's sweet wife had left a message of thanks and love for my care. Tears, for me, are necessary and cleansing and an immediate acknowledgment of my love for these patients.

As I walked the hospital halls to lunch one day, I heard screaming and saw a woman throw herself on the ground, saying, "No, no, no, it can't be!" A chaplain was helping her. I knew it was the trauma ICU waiting room and had just heard that a sixteen-year-old male had just come in after a random stabbing. I figured rightly that this was his mom and that she had just heard that he died in surgery. I was right, but my heart broke. I immediately broke into tears and had to go into a bathroom to compose myself and then was not hungry for lunch.

Feeling deeply another's pain will take something out of you, but the comfort you get from knowing you *feel* and *care* is what keeps you going. It's like the Grinch; your heart grows three sizes when you give a piece away and let yourself feel a stranger's pain or sorrow. There were many times I would go into a room to give bad news and the tears welling up in my eyes told the family way before I opened my mouth what the news was.

Emotion tends to rise up in a split second when something very deep changes in someone's life, whether good or bad. The privilege of nursing is to be there, in that moment, and to share this sacred feeling with that patient or family member. It makes life and health so much more precious to me and the lives I've had a glimpse into—so much more memorable and special to me. There are many ways to show true care; you do not have to be emotional or cry as easily as I do, but I know the Lord gave me this for a reason. The patients and families I've hugged and cried with *know* I loved them.

"Give, and it will be given to you. A good measure, pressed down, shaken together and running over, will be poured into your lap. For with the measure you use, it will be measured to you."

— Luke 6:38

TEACHING MOMENT

When you give a piece of your heart and are open with hurting people, it does take something from you and can cause pain. You will always get more back than you give if your compassion is given honestly and with love. Use the emotions you are blessed with; God gave them to us for a reason.

Debra Bauguess

LETTING GO.
NURSE, HEAL THYSELF

As an ICU RN, you see and hear things most people on this planet never will. A few other professions, like paramedics, EMTs, firefighters, police, MDs, and chaplains, also see both sides of humanity that very few see.

Number one: no matter how badly my own life may be going or what trials I'm living in, I came home humbled, blessed, and grateful after every single day at work. Families and patients in hospitals are undergoing procedures, surgery, death, tragedy, and trials at levels far more complex than mine. The heartbreak and stories you hear would make a grown man cry. The courage, strength, and resilience of most people have always amazed me. When you see young people after senseless life-altering accidents wake up forever altered by bad choices (drinking or drugs, mostly) or see the families left devastated by a loved one's moment of recklessness, you pause.

So many have been abused as children or had someone in their family murdered or lost parents or siblings to cancer at young ages. Even if the patient does well at the hospital, the family issues, struggles, and dysfunctions create new problems at home after the hospital discharge. I remember floating (when census in our home unit was low, we were sent to other ICUs needing help) to the trauma ICU and caring for a young girl who was comatose from a car versus pedestrian accident. At rounds (everyday meetings with all care providers to update and treat the patient), I heard her story. She had been emotionally and mentally abused by parents incapable of love. She had had Child Protective Services called numerous times on her situation. For whatever reason, they chose not to take her out of her environment. She then went and stood on the side of a busy freeway with writing on her hand saying, "Help me." She stepped in front of a car moving at high speed and now was in ICU, in a vegetative state, never to awaken. Her mom battled to gain control to keep her alive on life support against her daughter's wishes. I came home and sobbed that night and felt sick to my stomach for some time. Life does not seem fair.

I took care of a man in Mount Shasta ICU/CCU who had been shot point-blank with a shotgun in his stomach area by his sixteen-year-old daughter. The father was drunk and beating the mother for the umpteenth time, and the daughter just could not take it anymore. The man was in our ICU for over a month, as he had repeated surgeries to repair his bladder and intestines. Shotgun pellets were coming out of him with dressing changes for the entire month. His wife visited, and somehow, the man found truth and God in his time of healing. He chose life and Jesus and made up with his wife and changed his life overnight. A year later, I heard that his daughter had killed herself. She was unable to deal with the ramifications of what she had done.

In Mount Shasta, I saw small children after car crashes with grievous injuries. I saw the captain of the high-school football team come in with a self-inflicted gunshot wound to his head. I saw a young boy without a mark on him, lying brain-dead on the gurney after the tip of a falling tree hit the back of his head. His father was cutting a tree down too close to his wife and son (who were cutting their own tree down, both with chainsaws roaring). The wife and son did not hear the "Timber!" call from the father. They did rescue breathing for over one and a half hours in the middle of the woods before an ambulance could get there. The boy was unarousable and presumed brain-dead when we got him. I still wonder how both those parents lived with the guilt of that morning for the rest of their lives.

I took care of a young woman who had turned her life of addiction to heroin and methadone around and was clean. Her ex-boyfriend showed up to celebrate and suggested an IV drug that was "new and wonderful." It was called "krokodil." Within two days of shooting it in her arm, she started to lose skin, and it blackened and became dead tissue. After multiple surgeries, she now was minus her left shoulder, arm, breast, shoulder blade, clavicle, and pectoralis muscle (chest). With dressing changes, you could see her heart beating and lungs moving. The drug "krokodil" had similar ingredients to the sulfur in matchstick heads and gasoline. No wonder her living tissue took offense. She had given up a life of possibility after defeating drug addiction twice to end up like this for a one-time "fun" moment.

I took a young, seventeen-year-old boy to the operating room for organ donation after he became brain-dead from shooting up Speed with Gatorade. Someone had told him it was a better "high." His older "wiser" brother called me long-distance to ask about him. I gently told him his brother was brain-dead and why. (The mother had agreed to this; she wanted the word to get out about what this drug combo could do to others.) His brother said, "I know from personal experience that shooting up Gatorade with Speed cannot hurt you." I said, "I have it in personal experience that it *can* hurt you because your little brother will never wake up again." The brother just snorted on the phone and hung up, obviously thinking I was wrong. I wondered how long it would be before he was admitted to a hospital in the same condition. Many teenage friends were allowed to visit by the mother, who desperately wanted them to see what a choice like his could do to their life.

A young beautiful Russian girl who was nine months pregnant had her heart stop at home while she was sleeping. The husband did not know that her "gasps" were signs of impending death, and he did not know CPR. An ambulance was called, but it was too late by the time they got there. The wife and baby were without adequate oxygen for probably over half an hour. What people do not realize is that it only takes three to five minutes without oxygen for your brain cells to start irreversibly dying. The emergency room immediately took the baby out by C-section and sent the baby up to our neonatal ICU for a desperate chance at life. The mother came to our ICU. She was there for about a month, as was her baby in the neonatal ICU. They were both deeply vegetative, meaning their brains had been without oxygen for too long and both would never wake up. The family was there daily, praying for her to have a miracle that never came. We eventually transferred her and the baby to a downtown hospital for insurance purposes, where I heard they both were taken off life support after another long length of time (and died).

An LVN friend of mine let her son go swimming at the lake, and he dove into shallow water and broke his neck by hitting a rock with his head. She spent the rest of her life caring for him at home, now a quadriplegic.

Another LVN, and close friend, went to her brother's funeral in Texas. They hit an icy patch of road and spun out of control, ran off the highway, flipped, and survived it. As they waited for help, a garbage truck came by, hit the same icy patch, spun off the road at the same exact spot, and flipped over on them, killing her.

Fate played a terrible role in many of the accidents I saw the results of. Life is full of instantaneous changes that forever alter a family's future. Whether the reason is self-made or random does not ease the pain these people feel. The hardest patients to care for were the suicide attempts. One poor little dying man had written four pages of reasons why he wanted to die. He had followed an internet "how to kill yourself" teaching. His elderly wife found him purple in the garage, with a bag over his head and the car engine running. She called 911, and he ended up in our ICU for a brief period before ultimately dying. The saddest thing was that all the reasons on his list were signs of aging. He couldn't hear well, couldn't urinate well, couldn't walk well, was losing teeth, couldn't see well, and couldn't sleep well.

There is *no* good reason to take your own life, as it completely devastates the living family members. One young man hung himself, and one year later to the day, his mom hung herself. This left one sister to deal with both of these selfish acts.

A lovely woman came in with a small inferior wall myocardial infarction, very survivable for most people. She got the miracle drug tPA, which dissolves blood clots (because an MI is caused by a blood clot in an artery going to the heart muscle). She did better, had no pain, and was stable and eating lunch. Suddenly, she said, "I don't feel so well," and proceeded to die in front of us slowly. We all watched as her eyes became vacant and she slumped over within about one minute's time. There was nothing anyone could do; she had had a massive brain bleed from the clot dissolver.

Precious life is taken so quickly. If more people saw how quickly it can go, they might rethink their choices. A young mom with children wanted to win a radio show's prize by seeing how much water she could drink in a certain time. She drank so much water in such a short amount of time that her sodium levels drastically dropped, her brain swelled precipitously, and she died.

I could go on: so many more hard things happened over the entire forty-two years. I believe even more deeply in the sanctity of life and see how precious and short it is. We who see these things *must* take care of ourselves. We also need to learn to let go. The time we have with these patients and their families is brief, in the scope of life on this planet. That time is God-given and leaves a mark on our lives and hearts. Our lives would not have been as full or meaningful if we had not known or loved them.

I believe there is a reason for every single person who's placed in our lives. Unconditional love is given and received. A life without the loss you feel now means you would have never felt the caring and love that was exchanged between you and the patient or their family.

To "let go" does not mean you forget. On the contrary, you never, ever forget; you just move on to the next patient and get different love. You move on because that next patient needs a caring person to pour into their lives. You only let go to protect your heart so you can keep giving love and a piece of your heart to all who need it. If you never let go, your heart would be all used up. You just remember and learn and thank God these people were placed in your life for a short time. If you love and let go and relove and keep loving, your heart just gets stronger and able to love more. That means enough rest, proper diet, enough outlets through exercise, and release through reading, writing, gardening, hiking, fishing, etc. You need to renew your mind and soul.

For me, personally, it was always nature. Hiking on a beach, hearing the roar of surf with endless waves scouring the sand, grabbing at your toes while you smell the salt air and feel it on your skin gives me a sense of how small we are against the backdrop of an infinite ocean. Hiking a trail beside fragrant pine and fir trees with bees buzzing, birds singing, and a rock-strewn stream gurgling brings me a peace only the Creator can give. It renews and refreshes a weary heart that "saw too much" the last few months at work. I now also turn to God, the Word, and prayer. Peace is not elusive; you need to find out where your strength and renewal come from. Maybe it's music, riding horses, or taking a vacation. You, as a caregiver to the most hurting people on the planet, in ICUs, *need* to find an avenue that uplifts you to recharge your batteries. If you cannot handle it, go to some other less intense form of nursing. I chose to stay and do what I could do to alleviate a small portion of the suffering on this planet. I'm not noble or a saint; I'm as imperfect as the next person, but I deeply felt the calling to stay there.

When you are going through something at home or in your own life, it is the hardest time to *give of* yourself to others. A few times, I was going through an intense emotional storm at home—both parents facing care outside the home, a dad with dementia, a mom with failing health, my own failing marriage—and my capacity to react rationally or give love to other hurting people changed.

There are times to take a break away from work to heal yourself so you can eventually go back and serve and love others effectively again. My husband of four and a half years suddenly became schizophrenic in my midtwenties. He had an acute psychotic break almost overnight. Lightbulbs, TVs, and satellites were beaming things into his brain, telling him what to do, and spying on us. He talked and laughed to himself and wrote pages of gibberish. He woke up on Christmas Eve in 1983 and started beating me, forced himself on me, followed me to another room, and hit me some more. Then, he suddenly left to go into another room.

I sat on the floor in shock, wondering what to do, and I heard a voice. It was in my right ear and full of command and urgency. I looked to my right and saw no one. He said, "*Get out now!*" I jumped up, threw on a robe and slippers, ran out the back door, and slipped on the icy steps, cutting my knee. I ran to a neighbor's house, and they let me in, hysterical, crying, and bruised. I called the police to report it and remembered we had a gun with our camping gear. It was my grandfather's pearl-handled .38 revolver. I told the police to take the gun to the station and hold it and to get my husband out of the house so I could pack a bag and leave. I watched from the neighbor's window as the police knocked, the door opened, and my husband was standing there with the gun in his hand. I know to this day that God spoke to me and saved my life, or I would have been shot.

I was severely depressed for six months while I lived with my folks and didn't want to get up in the morning. I sought God and faith, started swimming, slowly gained strength, and moved to Sacramento to Mercy San Juan Hospital, where I worked for the next thirty-six years. It actually gave me great insight into domestic-abuse cases. I needed that time to regroup but eventually found that I *needed* to feel *needed* again and to help people. Thank You, Lord, for saving me!

Debra Bauguess

Violence in hospitals is increasing. I've been bitten in the shoulder by an elderly woman in DTs (*delirium tremens*—acute alcohol withdrawal), spit upon, kicked, scratched, and hit. Mostly it's from mental illness, brain damage (especially frontal lobe), DTs, or drug withdrawal. I went home with bruises many a night. We, at least, could call code grays to help. That is where several security guards or burly-type guys showed up to help you contain the situation.

I believe once God gives you a heart to care and want to help hurting people, it doesn't go away. You, as a person, have to want it, though. Please learn to counterbalance the hard things in life with the good by helping yourself first. It's like the airlines' saying, "In case of emergency, place the oxygen mask over your own face first, then over the faces of your children." If we are not okay first, we cannot help the hurting.

> *"I lift up my eyes to the mountains—where does my help come from? My help comes from the LORD, the Maker of heaven and earth."*
>
> — Psalm 121:1–2

> *"The LORD will keep you from all harm—he will watch over your life; the LORD will watch over your coming and going both now and forevermore."*
>
> — Psalm 121:7–8

TEACHING MOMENT

Find ways to release tension, anger, frustration, worry, and loss. Find a way to vent. It's okay to cry. Our profession sees and feels a great deal of human suffering. We also see joy and miracles. Make whatever renews and feeds your soul a priority after emotional days. You need to stay healthy to help all the others, including yourself and your own family.

COMMUNICATION AND HOW TO TALK ABOUT THE HARD THINGS

A touch is a powerful form of communication. It is a part of who I am. I hugged everyone; I held hands, stroked foreheads, and frequently kissed sweet little older people I cared about on their foreheads as they rolled out of the ICU. Many times, both the patient and I had tears in our eyes, and we may have only known each other for one to two twelve-hour shifts.

Silence is equally effective. When you don't know what or how to say it, don't. You don't need to talk to fill the silence; the silence speaks for itself. Sit closely, hold a hand, and listen. While they speak, just let them know you care.

More times than not, I would whisper a prayer under my breath for Jesus to give me strength and the right words upon entering a patient's room. It may be hard news, bad news, teaching, or encouragement you need to deliver. It's never about you; it's all about them. They have a perceived, very real quandary. There are so many questions about life and death that every single family asks.

I believe some of us develop a deeper comfort level to deal with loss or grieving than others. Maybe, it's the years spent seeing so much pain and loss. God gave me a heart to feel, care and the strength and wisdom to go into a room and get right to the honest truth of the matter. I learned to place myself in their shoes, walk in, and in the first few minutes, be open, honest, and gently blunt about the truth. I found patients and families to be far stronger in their ability to deal with hard things if they knew what they faced or had to think about right up front. Some family members, especially a spouse, would tell you, "I can't deal with it." I would respect that and be cautious with the amount of information I gave and how I delivered it. Much more often, people thanked me for up-front, open truth and honesty right from the beginning (at admission).

A wife with two children came in to find her husband had been brought in from work with a stroke. He was moderately affected and probably would never hold a job again and most likely would need care of some sort for the rest of his life. I grabbed a clipboard, a piece of paper, and a pen to give her and walked in. I said, "We know certain outcomes to be probable because of what we see all the time with people who have strokes like his. There is some hope, but very possibly, he won't be home for a long time [due to rehab] or work again." She was shocked and distraught, so I hugged her, let her cry, and said, "I can help right now." I asked if she wanted some guidance with priority setting. She said, "Oh yes, please."

We sat down, and I started asking her if she knew where their car and car keys were. I continued with questions: Did she have enough money to pay the mortgage? Did she have access to and know of bank accounts, due bills, trash days, etc.? I asked who she had to watch the kids while she stayed with her husband. I asked where she drew her strength from.

Once we got through a rough list of priorities, she started to cry and hugged me and said, "Thank you so much! My thoughts are splintered off in so many directions right now. I can't think straight." She added, "Now I can start somewhere. I have a plan to get me going in some direction instead of sitting and worrying."

Debra Bauguess

I used that tactic over and over again with great success. You initially need to validate their shock, anger, and hurt before you sit and "give the talk." You *must* gauge where they are mentally and emotionally before you discuss difficult topics. I would always initiate the talk with, "What do you know of your loved one's prognosis from what you've been told?" Many were up on details and very aware of most issues. Many more would say, "I haven't been told a lot" or "didn't understand most of what they said to me."

Many people in a strange, new environment, and possibly with a different culture or language, get stressed about the loved one's health problems and feel intimidated. Most just do not understand the medical jargon. They truly do not know what to ask or how to ask it. When you opened the door and asked, "What have you heard?" and "What do you understand?" the flood gates would open. They basically needed time, someone to care and sit with them and explain it in easy-to-understand language.

I would sit them down outside the room, sometimes at the computer, so I could show them a CT or MRI image (never breaking HIPAA). Seeing the damaged area gave them a much clearer understanding of what they were up against. I would give a brief open, honest picture of the prognosis, based on like situations with others in the same predicaments. I would listen, hug, cry, and pray (after asking if they wanted it): whatever they seemed to need at that moment.

Questions would come when their minds freed up from the shock of hearing unwelcome news. The hugs, touch, and prayer showed empathy and care. I would then try to propose a priority list or help them with what comes next. Next could be "wait and see" or more tests, procedures, and lab work. Unfortunately, in a neuro ICU, it was always "wait" because we "need much time for a swollen, hurt brain to try and heal, then we'll know more."

So many times, I gave hard news and had disastrous results. One father found out his only teenage son with recent flu had heart-and-lung damage (viral cardiomyopathy) that was so severe he'd need a heart and lung transplant to survive. He swung out with his fist. I ducked before he smashed his fist through the wall and broke into sobbing. He wasn't aiming for me, just overcome with grief and disbelief.

A husband's wife had a routine surgery and had an unforeseen complication that resulted in her death. He slumped down against me in a faint, to the floor, as I told him. The surgeon had called me and asked me to break the news.

A mom had a young son who had committed suicide (and was now comatose and probably brain-dead on life support). As I broke the news to her, she screamed and fell to the floor. She was hysterical, crying and yelling and threatening, over and over, to kill herself after she left. We had to lift her into a wheelchair. After she saw her son, we were convinced she would try to hurt herself at home, so we had to take her to the emergency room to be mentally evaluated.

Some doctors are very good at bad news, but many are not. Some ask the nurse to give it. I've unfortunately been in that position many times.

I responded to a code blue (emergency response for a dying patient) on another unit and saw that it was the husband of a friend of mine. She was a ward clerk in the trauma ICU and was sitting outside the closed room as we did CPR on her husband. The cardiologist and I, running the code, saw the signs of catastrophic nonresponse in front of us. The patient was in

Debra Bauguess

asystole (no viable heart rhythm). He was "blue" from the waist up, usually indicating some kind of overwhelming failure to get blood to half his body. We felt it had been a massive blood clot blocking a major artery somewhere, and there was nothing we could continue to do for him. Nothing, in the approximately thirty minutes of CPR, had any effect. We called an end to the code, and the MD asked me to tell her, as he couldn't. We both had known her a long time. I said a prayer and stepped outside to see in her eyes that she knew, probably from my face. We hugged and cried, and I had her go in to see him. That was one of the hardest times for me. I felt the grace she offered me in her response to the terrible news I gave her.

Another time, a young man in his forties had gone to his construction job while he had the flu. He had type one diabetes and didn't hydrate or heed his symptoms, fell unconscious, and ended up in our CCU. He had a wife and two small kids. I got close to her as I took care of him. I took him for an MRI two days into his care (he had not woken up and was on life support). I legally cannot give results or read an MRI or CT but have enough experience to know when it's *not* good—as in "probably brain-dead."

I took him back to his room, and his wife asked what it showed. I said we had to wait for the radiologist and neurologist to read the scan. She kept looking at me as I hooked up IVs and straightened the room. I could not look her in the eyes. I left the room and went and hid in a supply room, afraid to face her and give her the truth. After a prayer, I went back into his room, looked at her, teared up, and said, "I can't give you actual results, but it isn't good." She stood up, started crying, and screamed at me, "That's not what I wanted to hear,

Debbie!" I cried and said, "I'm so sorry, it's not what I wanted to tell you."

A few weeks after he was taken off life support and died, I sent a card to her, expressing sympathy. I asked many patients if they would allow me to send a card in the future to see how they were. They always said yes. I told her I had hidden in the supply room, afraid to give her the bad news. She said she saw me and knew and thanked me for at least telling her it was worse before the MD told her he was brain-dead. I learned from that to a least say, "It's better," "worse," or "the same" while families waited for news, without divulging actual details. They needed truth, and the MDs who knew my years of experience and manner with people were more than happy for me to break the ice before they arrived.

It's never going to be easy to give hard news, but with experience, placing myself in their shoes, and asking for wisdom to use the right words, I learned how to do it with compassion. I know what I would want to hear, know, and feel if I were in the same situation. I had a housekeeper, a dear friend, tell me she had always wished I could be her nurse if she was sick. She had seen me in action, giving the talk to a distraught family member outside a room many times.

Communication is all about the timing, the attitude of the "giver," and the emotional state of the "hearer." There were times I got to give miraculous news about healing and a turnaround in a patient's condition.

Once I took care of a young woman who had been an all-star army fitness expert. She ended up in our ICU with overwhelming sepsis (bloodstream infection) from an abdominal infection. I took care of her many times and got very close to her mom. She worsened and, after more than a week, was now on life support. We had multiple IV drips, central lines, and a breathing machine on very high settings (max life support for someone with ARDS, or adult respiratory distress syndrome). She "blew up" like the Michelin Man from her critical state. The body "leaks" fluids into tissues, and it swells and enlarges to where you can triple in size very fast. You then risk severe organ failure (liver, kidneys, heart, gut, etc.) from the pressure of the swelling tissues.

She had another surgery to "open" her belly to relieve abdominal pressure and increase blood flow to her organs. She literally was on the brink of death one day. I told her mom to pray because I felt that if we didn't see a change in her condition by the midpoint of our twelve-hour shift, she wouldn't make it. We had reached the peak of human, medical intervention and had nothing left to help her with but time. All our attempts were not enough. The mom prayed, and I prayed.

Halfway through the shift, I saw subtle changes showing that the patient was "fighting back." Her youth, fitness level, fierce willpower to live, and extreme medical intervention, with prayer, came through for her. Another hour passed, and she continued to show signs of improvement. They were subtle, and she was still severely ill, on life support. I remember hugging her mom as I said, "God heard our prayers, and she's turning the corner." We cried. It took two or three weeks more for her to recover slowly to where she could even walk again.

I used to take her treats and go up to her medical floor room and talk with her and tell her what a miracle she was. I could tell she was depressed at feeling so weak. She did recover and only had two fingertips that had blackened (dead-tissue) areas that sloughed off. She was fine. She and I shared a special bond because I poured into her *after* ICU. I encouraged her and loved on her. She used to hug me and cry and tell me she would have never made it without me.

Thank You, Lord. Different caregivers have different strengths. I found that years of experience with death, tragedy, grieving, and loss greatly helped my credibility. Families were comforted by my nursing knowledge being over forty years.

Many caregivers are not "touchy" or "huggers." Many cannot give bad news and leave it to the MD. However it's done, the patient or family's dynamics and strengths need to be assessed and taken into consideration. I would wait for the right moment to go into a room and speak on hard things. I would prepare them gently, and many would know right then that all was not well. Whatever your technique is, use extreme kindness, compassion, and empathy. Truth and honesty are best. It's good to use fewer words; the more you circle around what you are trying to say, the more anxious they get. Get to the point and *always* place yourself in their position and think about what you would want to hear and how you would want to hear it. It's never going to be easy for you or them. It does come more comfortably, though, with experience when you have done it many times before.

> *"Administer true justice; show mercy and compassion to one another."*
>
> — Zechariah 7:9

TEACHING MOMENT

Watch how other nurses and MDs talk to patients. Learn from them. Some are more effective than others. Pick up on clues;

learn tact, gentleness, honesty, timing, and above all, use love in relaying any hard news. If they *feel* that you care, your exact words aren't as important. Don't give up on yourself if you are unable to give bad news easily or well. It took me years! Use what strengths you've been given to ease the hard situation for them and yourself.

DEATH IS A PART OF LIFE

I didn't start nursing, expecting to see death, but knew I would at some point. I didn't really face it until the first time a patient died, who I had truly cared about and had invested love into. He was a retired cop. He was scruffily bearded and bighearted and sweet to me but was dying from cancer. After several weeks of our caring for him, he suddenly coded (his heart stopped) one night. I remember standing at the bedside with my mentor holding me as I cried. That was the first time I thought, *Bad things happen to good people.* I can't say death became easy to deal with, but my job required the expertise to *run* toward the crisis and *know* what to do and do it to the best of my ability.

Certain deaths, of course, were harder: children of any age; sudden, tragic death at any age; fellow coworkers and friends; senseless accidents, whether random shooting, drunken drivers, murder, or suicides, and of course, family. Watching the light go out of someone's eyes as they are talking with you, having their hand slip out of yours while you are watching the blood pressure drop or the heart rate slow and flatten never ceased to affect me. I remember watching an open-heart surgery where they push potassium chloride into your IV and dump sterile ice water into an open chest with an already fibrillating (quivering, not beating effectively) heart to stop it. I learned coronary bypass is basically a carefully controlled death. When the miraculous surgery was over, just the process of letting the patient's body rewarm by itself would make the heart start pumping by itself. I remember crying at the miracle of taking and giving back life.

Veterans have long known the value of life. My dad flew reconnaissance missions in Vietnam and found five or six marines stranded behind enemy lines. He called in their position and saved them. He received a plaque with an M16 mounted on it, saying something like, "Life has a special flavor; only those that fight for it will ever know."

Death *is* a part of life. The absence of life *is* death, just as the absence of light is dark, the absence of health is illness, or the absence of fear is hope. It is not to be expected or looked forward to but will happen to all of us. We should all wish to die with dignity, and hopefully, without suffering. I remember a baby with marasmus (failure to thrive) at Travis Air Force Base when I was a candy striper in the hospital. The baby wasn't being fed. The parents did not know they had to feed it. I question the mental IQ of many young people having babies. The baby was placed into a capable foster home with multiple other children but did not survive and died due to a lack of love. He got food and a warm bed, but not enough cuddling, attention, and pure love was given to him. Children with fractures (legs, arms) would adamantly deny the parent had done it, even though their medical history showed repeated injuries, fractures, and bruises. They would say, "I fell off the bed" because they only knew abuse as love. They were loyal to the parents who abused them and would lie to us to stay with them. I remember a two-month-old baby with a fractured skull. I think he survived, but his "loving" father had dropped him headfirst on concrete. He was a young GI who didn't want a kid to watch. It broke my heart and made me not want to do pediatrics.

Debra Bauguess

Some death is timely and needed and provides a way to end great suffering. At Mount Shasta Hospital, I had a wonderful older schoolteacher as a patient. She had pancreatic cancer (almost always fatal). She was in our ICU for quite some time with intense pain due to the enzymes in her sick pancreas "eating her" from the inside out. She wanted to die and not have more suffering, but her husband sat by her bedside day after day, saying, "I need you; don't go, don't leave me." It was difficult to watch both of them. We tried to help him understand, but it was tough because they had been married for so many years. One day, as she was barely conscious, he said to her, "It's okay, honey. I'll be okay; you can go now." She died peacefully within about one minute of hearing him. She had only hung on for him. It was a blessing to see her heart rate slow and stop. The husband actually did well by this time; he truly was ready to let her go.

My dad had dementia his last few years. He was such a smart man, an air force pilot and flying instructor, who loved crosswords and math. He became forgetful, stumbled and shuffled along, and could not carry a sentence at the end. He was a very proud man and would *not* have elected to live this way. He had to be taken to a memory care unit, as he had diabetes, incontinence, and could not walk very well. It was heartbreaking to see him and then have to drive away. He would go from window to window, waving and blowing kisses to us, not understanding why we were leaving him there. I would cry. I still regret having to take him from his home of over forty years, away from his wife of over sixty years, to a strange place to be left all alone, not understanding.

At the end, he had a heart attack, an irregular heart rhythm, and I believe, a small stroke. The last time I saw him, he was incoherent and drooling and choking on water, unable to move one side well. I knew, as a nurse of many years, death was close. This was Friday, and I had to work twelve-hour shifts an hour away on Saturday and Sunday. On Saturday, my sister-in-law and nephews saw him, and he was coherent and loving and said he loved my brother and me so much. He said, "Love is all there is at the end." On Sunday, a woman at my church told me she "saw" God holding out his arms to Dad and God placing a mantle of comfort over me. My dad died the next day.

I'm still dealing with not having been there. I should have called in sick and stayed with him, even not knowing exactly when he'd die. At least, he was at peace. One year or so after my dad died, I had two different instances where little older men gave me a glimpse of my dad. One patient was moved out of ICU to a floor bed, and as I left, I said, "I hope you do well and go home soon." He said, "You betcha," and gave me a wink and a look that was my dad's look. My dad used to say this and give that specific look. I caught my breath and felt the Lord had given me a glimpse of my dad to comfort me and let me know he was okay and watching me from heaven. Another older man had the same name, Kenneth. I said, "That was my dad's name." He gave me another "Dad" look and said, "It's a good name." Again, the saying and the look were from my dad—from God to me—for comfort.

We see estrangement at the time of death, and it's so sad. Families that haven't spoken to kids, siblings, moms, or dads in years would refuse, often, to let us at least call their family members to inform them of their imminent death. Please, if you know anyone who is aging and unreconciled to a loved one, do what you can to help prevent this deathbed tragedy.

Debra Bauguess

It's so senseless at that time. Unforgiveness, resentment, regret, and hurt are so very damaging to the ones left alive.

Patients used to see tunnels, bright light, and loved ones at the brink. One man said, "Nurse, quick, put down the side rail; the angel of the Lord is here to take me." I looked behind me and, of course, saw nothing. I turned toward the patient, and he was "gone."

Late one night shift in a dark ICU, my elderly patient died of expected causes. As the LVN with more than thirty years of experience helped me (myself with two years of experience) turn the patient to put them in a body bag, a loud moan came out of the patient. I screamed and jumped back while the LVN laughed. She said, "Have you never heard the air leave the lungs when you turn a dead person?" Of course, I hadn't. The comfort level with death and dying comes with time and dealing with it over and over again, and seeing and hearing many things others will never see.

We used to deal with different cultures. Some Asian cultures wanted the finest clothing on their loved ones before death. It took some challenges to get beautiful clothes over tubes, catheters, and monitor wires, but we did our best. Some would close the door and chant for many hours, while others would pray loudly. Gypsies would fight to be in the room, touching the "king" or "queen" gypsy as they died because if they were the last one touching them, they would then become the next king or queen.

Many years of experience did give me more comfort in dealing with death and grieving families. Younger nurses did not particularly know how or like to deal with it. I was once there myself. I believe death is not something to be feared. Of course, I, and no one else I know, want a slow lingering death or great suffering before death. Everyone should think at some point about where they go after death, make decisions for the family, and start paperwork after a certain age to clarify wishes for after you are gone. I saw way too many times a spouse (usually a wife), suddenly now not knowing what accounts they had. Where are the spare car keys, what day does the trash go out, or where is any of the paperwork for bills, car and house insurance, car title and registration, bank accounts, computer passwords, taxes, etc.? Having to deal with the sudden loss of the one who knew all that, and deal with not knowing what to do or where to begin, added a double portion of stress for these people. Please think ahead enough about mortality so that you plan for spouses and children and discuss wishes *before* it happens.

I'm dealing with a young woman right now (in retirement, as part of a compassion team at church) who is dying within a year or so of cancer. She has just found out and is being so very strong and wise about dealing with this. She's creating memories, writing letters, and making videos for loved ones to encourage them in years to come. It's heartbreaking and yet so beautiful to discuss your wishes openly for a future you will not be part of. She's actually teaching me how to die gracefully. People like her are why I love nursing.

To end this talk about death, I must say it's a privilege to be with someone at their entrance to life (baby being born) and returning from death (post-CPR, when they wake up), and upon the moment they draw their last breath. A long time ago, we had a little older homeless man dying of AIDS and pneumonia. He was a DNR (allow to die naturally; do not use any extraordinary means of life support). He had no family. We were all busy, and I heard the ward clerk say, "Look, his heart rate is slowing; he's dying, and no one is with him." I felt a deep conviction and ran into the room and held his hand while he died. From that moment on, *none* of my patients ever died alone. That became especially important later, during the COVID-19 year, as our nation would not let loved ones in while their family died. The nurses became family and were with the patients when they went to meet their Maker. It was not fair or moral and should *never, ever* happen again.

> *"Therefore, my dear brothers and sisters, stand firm. Let nothing move you. Always give yourselves fully to the work of the LORD, because you know that your labor in the LORD is not in vain."*
>
> — 1 Corinthians 15:58

TEACHING MOMENT

Death happens to us all. You cannot stop every patient from dying. If the family knows you care and give honest information, their burden will be eased. In time and with practice, you can learn to say difficult things with love to hurting people. Evaluate your own feelings about death as it relates to you and your patients. Take classes, if necessary, to understand what the body goes through as it dies. Families ask about that all the time.

CODE BLUE AND ETHICS

This is a touchy subject. It's so easy for health professionals to understand but very difficult for nonmedical people. Most people think not doing emergency life-support measures on a dying patient is wrong. I, personally, do not want someone shocking me, doing CPR, and fracturing ribs or putting me on a breathing machine if my body and brain are not going to be viable. Quality of life is a huge issue. Some families want their loved ones alive as long as possible, just because *they* cannot let go. It's about them, not the wishes of the loved one. I truly do not want to offend anyone, but please put the wishes of your dying loved one first. If they have a terminal disease and their time has come, let us give them comfort in the passing and allow them to die with dignity. When it becomes about your wants, the loved one suffers and endures prolonged, unnecessary pain at their expense for your wishes.

Basically, if someone is trying to die, you either do everything or nothing; the "partial" codes do not work. You cannot give emergency meds and not circulate the blood with the meds in it by CPR. CPR does not help without the shock and the meds. Breathing for them does not prolong life without circulation, meds, CPR, and shocking the heart. The nurse's role is to educate gently, comfort, answer questions, and guide toward what the patient would want. Many patients died with dignity, and many patients died with prolonged suffering due to the family's misunderstanding or selfishness. Some "family,"

I use the term loosely, kept a relative alive needlessly because they were living off their social security at home. This is where our ethics committee and family meetings in the ICU would help. The ethics group and ICU family meeting group would listen to multiple family members and guide, never push, toward love, dignity, and respect for the dying loved one's wishes. We never went against a family's wishes, even if we did not agree.

The only time you can refuse further care is if the patient is pronounced brain-dead by two MDs. This is state law. I'm glad to say many families understood and loved and respected their dying loved one's wishes. They gave every action and thought to ease his or her passage from this life to the next. Many were actually beautiful, tender, heart-touching moments of unconditional love, where we became a part of it. To anyone reading this: please discuss with your family your wishes and concerns about suffering and make it known by a living will, power of attorney, POLST, power of healthcare, or any other legal form of a document—*before it happens.*

Also, consider becoming an organ donor. Your soul is gone, and the organs and tissues can save many lives. Blind people see; deaf people hear, and dying people needing hearts, lungs, livers, or kidneys live whole new lives. Your loved one "lives on," giving this precious gift of life to someone else. One healthy but, sadly, brain-dead person can save six or eight lives. Donorship gives some meaning to the death of your loved one. Consider whether you want extraordinary lifesaving drastic measures done if there is no chance of a viable quality recovery. Once that car accident happens or a heart stops, it is too late; if wishes are not known, it only gives the living family members extra stress to deal with at an already terrible moment.

Debra Bauguess

This is one of the most often dealt-with problems in ICU, and we always support the family. Our desires are not a part of it, though we will guide you into placing your loved one's wishes first, before yours. It is a sensitive subject and not one most people ever want to deal with. Place yourself in their shoes: How would you settle it if it was your wife, son, or daughter left to deal with your catastrophic stroke? Many patients are left in long-term care facilities in a terminally vegetative state where families cannot pay for them. It is tragic and leaves a legacy of pain and bitterness and long-drawn-out suffering for all involved. I beg you to talk with loved ones and be open, loving, and clear about death. It *is* a part of life. We will all be there someday.

> *"The last enemy to be destroyed is death."*
>
> 1 Corinthians 15:26

> *"Who can live and not see death, or who can save escape the power of the grave?"*
>
> — Psalm 89:48

> *Even though I walk through the darkest valley, I will fear no evil, for you are with me; your rod and your staff, they comfort me. You prepare a table before me in the presence of my enemies. You anoint my head with oil; my cup overflows. Surely goodness and love will follow me all the days of my life, and I will dwell in the house of the LORD forever.*
>
> — Psalm 23:4–6

TEACHING MOMENT

Think about your own wishes and your family's wishes upon death. Honor other families' wishes; just be sure you address them *before* the patient tries to die (if possible). Do not push or make a family feel bad for their choice, no matter how you feel about it. If the whole subject of death is too hard for you, do not go into ICU.

You will see death in life around you, whether your own family or a clinic setting: it is a part of life. Really search your heart for your feelings about it before you face it in your life or job.

Debra Bauguess

HUMOR

Not to be irreverent after a chapter on death—but there is always humor. Sickness and death are not humorous, but humor had its place because we, as the care team, dealt with life and death daily. We would have gone nuts ourselves without some stress relief in intense moments. Suffice to say, many cardiologists at Mercy San Juan Hospital are glad I'm not around on April fool's day because of the tricks I used to play on them, many that worked too well. I remember a fellow RN putting a smashed Tootsie Roll candy in a small plastic specimen jar with some apple juice. It looked like a urine specimen with stool in it. She then asked a doctor (known to be rather humorless) if he knew of any other way to test for sugar in it other than the lab. He said no. She then opened it and took a sip. He just about fainted.

I put some wasabi-fried peas in a specimen cup and asked a quiet MD if he's ever seen calcified bile stones. He said he hadn't. I proceeded to open the cup and eat one. He was horrified, and I felt guilty because he was so sweet.

How is it that little older ladies are the most foul-mouthed and strongest when confused? One such patient was screaming, kicking, and hitting in her extreme confusion, and she watched five or six of us rush in with our blue uniforms on to keep her in the bed and safe. She proceeded to yell, "You are all blue sleazy snakes." Another rather plump RN dashed in, and the patient yelled, "You're all *fat* blue sleazy snakes." We called ourselves that for a long time; it was our motto.

As I helped an MD discontinue an arterial line from a patient's groin, she yelled at me, "Stop it; you're such an ostrich!" The head cardiologist MD (and my friend) just looked at me and said, "Ostrich?" I guess it was the worst word she could think of.

Once, I dared to fool a head cardiac surgeon with a water-squirting calculator. I asked Dr. R. to push a button, and it squirted him in the eye. A moment of silence went by as I wondered if I'd gone too far. He started laughing and kept pushing it, squirting himself over and over, and wanted to buy one. Whew! We actually became friends after this, and I was never scared of him again. (He had a reputation for being rough on the nurses.)

One day, an elderly woman tiptoed barefooted into our CCU with her bare buttocks showing in the gown's back opening as she carefully carried a small paper bag. She was not from our unit, and we asked her where she was going. She said, "Ssshhh, I'm going home." She headed for the back fifth-floor stairwell. We gently turned her around toward her real room and asked what was in the bag. She said, "Why, dearie, it's my clean underwear for tomorrow."

My RN friend and I loved baseball (in the late '70s, when the Oakland Athletics were big). That night, a game was on TV. One elderly, confused lady kept trying to get up and calling out. A fellow RN and I went and sat on either side of the bed, and each held one of her hands. We asked if she liked baseball. She said, "Oh yes." We put the game on and showed her how to do the "wave." After about twenty minutes of nonstop three-person waving, we were exhausted and had to do other things. The patient was so happy to have friends who

Debra Bauguess

appreciated her unique ability to do the "wave" at the game. She'd worn herself out and slept well after that.

On the telemetry floor (where you are monitored for heart), an elderly wife came in about eight p.m. to do her husband's evening prebedtime care. He was confused and a patient there. She proceeded into the room, gave a soothing shave, washed his face, brushed his teeth, rubbed his back, and then started screaming, "This isn't my husband! What have you done with my husband?" Her husband was next door, still waiting. The gentleman she had lavished all the attention on sat there with the most glorious look of contentment on his face. He hadn't said one word the whole time. I have to wonder at the confusion of the wife, who didn't recognize her own husband up close.

My RN friend and I went to check on an elderly lady that was immobile, not looking responsive. We evaluated her for consciousness and couldn't arouse her. We started thinking it was a stroke and tried various methods to wake her up: shouting, finger pinching, and holding her arm up in the air to see if there was any tone in her arm. Her arm flopped to the bed. As we opened her eyelids to check her pupils, she said, "Leave me alone; I'm dead." So, we left her alone since she wanted to play dead. She was stable otherwise.

I once saw a progress note on a patient who was admitted with a mystery diagnosis. The note started out, "Thirty-two-year-old BM..." We all immediately knew the diagnosis: he had a thirty-two-year-old bowel movement still inside! ("BM" meant "Black male.") My favorite progress note of all time, by one of my dearest friends and most admired MDs, was, "We have a tiger by the tail; we cannot hang on, and we cannot let go." It was so perfect for the very critically ill patient because he was so very sick we couldn't stop trying to fix him, *but* he was so very sick we couldn't fix him!

A pulmonologist I respected, who used to drive me nuts, wanted to extubate, or pull out a breathing tube from a patient on a ventilator (breathing machine). We discussed in a very dignified way our reasons for doing it or not doing it. I knew the patient was borderline as far as his ability to breathe safely on his own without the airway. The older, wiser MD knew he had to try it at least. I disagreed, and the airway was pulled out. The patient had some difficulty and was breathing a little hard and needed extra oxygen, but he held his own. The next day, my day off, I returned home after running errands, and there was a message on my machine. "Debbie, the patient you did not want to extubate yesterday is doing *just fine*. I wanted to let you know." I want to know who gave that pesky doc my home phone number. To this day, actually, we are friends, and he even told me at a Christmas party I was his favorite. I honestly don't know if it was alcohol talking or true. I still love him.

In the first year of my career, I was told to irrigate a new colostomy. The patient was a local parish priest and had a new surgically placed colostomy. I couldn't find immediate help and did not know how to do it but figured it couldn't be too hard. First, I noticed the bag was all puffed up with air, looking like it would explode. Since I was a brand-new nurse, able to solve my own problems, I grabbed a safety pin and punctured the bag to let all the pressure out before it exploded. I learned very quickly that a colostomy bag full of "air" is *gas* produced by the intestines and does *not* smell very good (as I got a faceful). Over the next half hour, I tried to irrigate this new colostomy gently, and by the end, there was poop on me, poop on the priest, poop on the bed, and poop on the floor. I looked at him in shock and mortification and said, "I'm so sorry, I'll clean this up right away." We caught each other's eyes and started giggling and couldn't stop. I'm sure he knew all along I was new and inexperienced, and he was willing to "go with the flow." It got cleaned up, and I learned two valuable lessons: (1) if you don't know how to do something, ask first, and (2) any horrible situation can result in a friendship. He was a very gracious, sweet man, and I took care of him on another admission where he fainted against me as I walked him in a hallway. We became friends and corresponded, and he even gave me a wedding gift one year later.

In Mount Shasta, I was giving blood to an ICU post-op patient who had a big bowel surgery. His hemoglobin and hematocrit were low (he'd lost a fair amount of blood in surgery), and he needed it right away. We didn't have pumps to run blood through in those days, so I placed a pressure bag over the blood bag and pumped air into the pressure bag to push on the blood bag to run it faster. Well, evidently, I hadn't placed the blood-tubing spike all the way into the blood bag, and as I pumped up the pressure, the spike pulled out, and the blood bag exploded all over the patient, me, the walls, bed, and floor. We looked at the blood splatter in horror, and both started giggling. I quickly apologized, got everything cleaned up, and hung a new unit of blood.

He was an inspector that manned the inspection station on Interstate 5 just south of Mount Shasta. I drove through it every night after work at 12:30 a.m. When he was better, I would see him at the inspection station on my way home and say, "Hi." We always had a special connection. One night, there was a huge snowstorm, the kind where there's no wind, just huge fat flakes of snow, gently falling. I lived about twenty miles south of Mount Shasta, in Castella. It was falling heavily. I put chains on my 1970s old Ford Maverick under the ER carport and started off. My friend at the inspection station said, "I see your chains, Interstate 5 is closed to all traffic, but if you go slowly and steadily and go straight home, you'll just make it." I drove thirty miles per hour in thick falling snow with my car window down. There were about six inches of fluffy snow on the freeway. I was the only car in a silent white world on a normally busy interstate, and it was one of the most profoundly beautiful nights of my entire life. I never felt in danger; my friend said I'd make it, and I did. By morning, it was still snowing, and three days later, we had three feet of snow. I was snowed in and could not get out of the garage onto the freeway. Our exit and side streets were not plowed. My friend, who I'd exploded blood on, got me home. By the way, that mistake *never* happened again.

I once saw a fellow RN on her knees, looking under a curtain into her patient's room. I got down low and said, "Whatcha looking for?" She said, "I don't see my patient's feet." We looked in the room, and the patient was gone. We looked out the ground-floor window, and he was off to the side, smoking. He'd climbed out the window. We waited for ten minutes, and he was back outside the window, knocking to come back in for dinner.

At Mercy San Juan, a patient in the CCU wanted to smoke. He stood on his toilet in the alcove in his patient room, with his monitor cable snaking across the floor, and pulled the curtain across. He lit up his cigarette, and we smelled smoke. We followed the monitor cable, dangling above the floor all the way to the underside of the curtain around the toilet. He was puffing furiously while balancing on his toilet. He thought we

Debra Bauguess

didn't know he was hiding and smoking. I have to wonder at the desperation of some of these people, as well as their IQs.

We had a hundred-year-old gentleman who was very confused, sitting in a chair outside his room, carefully tied by a sheet to the chair, so he would not fall. He was very wobbly. I took care of him the entire shift, and he kept calling my name, "Debbie, marry me." Everyone else thought it was so very funny. As I finished reporting to the night RN and was leaving, I heard her go to him and introduce herself as "Debbie." Her name was not "Debbie." Two days later, after *all* the nurses told him their names were "Debbie," he was still screaming out, "Debbie, come marry me now." I'm so glad I could provide humor at my expense.

As long as you never used humor at someone's expense or to make fun of them, it served its place. Patients used to beg to be a part of our silliness and practical jokes, often instigating pranks. One little lady begged us for a squirt bottle and got her nurse several times, giggling like a two-year-old each time. I always asked the men on admission paperwork if they were pregnant or breastfeeding. There are so many gentle ways to cut through the fear and tension with silly remarks. I'll never forget the sight of the naked rear end of a man running out the back emergency exit because he needed to be "out of there." Humor, tastefully done, defuses pain, horror, and anguish. It strips tension. It will definitely always play a role in healthcare.

"[…] *A time to weep and a time to laugh*"

— Ecclesiastes 3:4

TEACHING MOMENT

Be judicious and careful with the setting, but there is a time for humor. Just be respectful. Not everyone views what is humorous to you the same way. Never do it at someone else's expense. Be aware of the setting: someone nearby may be grieving or dying. Let the patients be in on your gag if possible and they want to. It lifts their spirits immensely.

A PIECE OF
MY HEART—SHARING
YOUR LIFE

A heart is a vital organ in the bodies of each of us. It pumps up to a hundred years for some and sends the blood with the life-giving oxygen to our needy cells. It is the life source of our love and emotions and helps us find the good in others. I learned a long time ago you reap what you sow; you get reward and satisfaction in accordance with how much effort and love you give. The more hurting the person is, the more you get back because they *needed* you. To give, when it is needed, changes you and the person you help. When I say I give a piece of my heart, I mean I have to expose my life and shine a light inside and share something familiar, similar, funny, or meaningful with that hurting person. If someone in pain or grieving can, just for one moment, connect with another human being's life, it brings them out of themselves and puts them back in the world of the living. When you open up to another, you take the chance of letting in hurt, pain, joy, sorrow, and happiness. When you give enough of yourself and try hard enough, usually, you can "get through" to that hurting person in the bed or family member. The warmth you get when they reciprocate and share back is priceless. I used to spend many hours in a shift, trying different sharing tactics and stories to find the right one to get the patient to open up. Only when you try hard enough, and it works, do you and the patient forge a friendship, a kindred spirit, and an atmosphere of healing. It's strange how I look back at the thousands of pieces of my heart I have given away to human beings who desperately needed it, and now I have a heart more *full* than ever before. I will never get enough of the joy that comes with knowing you did your best to help someone and they responded.

I was ministered right back to many times. It's amazing how love, freely given, never returns void. If you are too shy or too fearful of feeling someone else's pain or sorrow, maybe nursing in ICU is not for you. This concept of giving a piece of your heart to someone who needs you goes far beyond the hospital. It blesses the giver as much as the recipient if it's given with the right attitude.

I had a student come to me and complain that her patient was needy and on her light constantly. I said, "Do you know why she's that way?" She said, "No, she's just irritable and needy, and I don't want to go back in there." I said, "You go in there, pull up a chair close to her, and say, 'I know you're probably scared and in pain. Can I help because I care?' Also, find a subject you have in common like gardening, books, pets, travel, sports, flowers, etc. Share a piece of your life experience with her and ask about hers." About a half hour later, my student came back and said, "Wow, she's such a nice lady, we talked about…, and I like…, and she likes…; I like her." Needless to say, the light only went off for "needs" a couple more times, not every five minutes. People need to feel seen, cared for, special, and important to you. It's such an easy thing to do; just put yourself in their shoes. Try to figure out all the possible reasons they are acting out. It's usually fear, pain, loss, change, loss of control, missing home, pets, loved ones, etc. We, after all, are all human, with very real perceived needs, wishes, wants, and desires.

Debra Bauguess

Be a detective and when you figure out part of the reason or story, go sit down and talk, like a friend, and ask how they feel. Validate their fears, hopes, dreams, and disappointments. Tell them you will do your best. It was hard with twelve-hour shifts because you frequently had them only two days in a row or were off the next three days. This was interrupted continuity versus the five-day-a-week-eight-hour-a-day RN. I made a point of calling in on my day off to ask the RN to tell the patient I cared and was praying. Sometimes, I came in on a day off and visited. Your actions speak so much louder than words. They see and feel that you really care. To this day, it gives me joy and fulfillment.

In retirement, now, I miss very little about work, except the joy of pouring into a life that needed help. I'm now joining the compassion team at my church. I will be making phone calls to isolated, hurting people and eventually going back into hospitals where my comfort level is high. I will visit, comfort, cheer up, pray, and share my heart again with those who need me. Three days before I retired, a young woman and her father came in to visit their dying mom/wife. I grew very close and came in on my day off to help the family with turning off life support. As I hugged the daughter before I left the room, I said, "I don't know why I'm so drawn to you and your dad, but I am. I care and will pray for you." She said, "I know why you were drawn to us; it's because we *needed* you." I cried. It was the culmination of my entire forty-two-year career.

God gave me a heart to love and a need to share it. That is why I was drawn to hurting people—they needed a touch from a caring person. Wow, God is good. She and I still correspond to this day; I love her and still pray for her.

Don't be scared to feel pain; it's only in the sharing of the patient's and family's pain that you grow and strengthen and change into the kind of nurse hurting people need.

"But those who hope in the LORD will renew their strength. They will soar on wings like eagles; they will run and not grow weary, the will walk and not be faint."

— Isaiah 40:31

TEACHING MOMENT

Sharing a piece of your life is difficult for some, but I guarantee you the patient feels that you care if you even try to understand their side of it. Your openness to share your life gives them hope in not being the only one suffering. You don't have to give details about your life if you don't want to but can share simple things you have in common, like reading or flowers or animals. If a patient knows you've been through something similar (never exactly the same as them, though), they bond over shared experiences.

GIVING AND RECEIVING

God gives in love and ministers to, of His own free will. Many years ago, I found the power of going "out of my way" to give something extra to someone, needing a reminder that they are cared about. After all, it is only in the giving that we receive. I remember a wonderful woman with late-stage cancer. She'd been getting either chemo and/or radiation and had lost most of her hair. She'd not eaten much or even had an appetite for many days. She mentioned she loved a special kind of soup at a certain Chinese restaurant. On my day off, I went and got a large portion and took it to her. The look of gratitude in her eyes will stay with me forever. I think the time I spent chatting with her meant more.

I took care of a homeless man who lived in a storage shed. He rode a bike to landscaping jobs. He had the most beautiful blue eyes and an open manner. He'd been in the navy and served on a ship. I have a heart for veterans, as my dad was an air force pilot for twenty years and spent over a year in Vietnam. The patient had been hit on his bike by a car, and he'd fractured his collarbone and skull. He was stable but would have to live with his brother until he was able to work again. I thought, *Thank God he has a brother willing and able to take him in.*

I had a lot of "firsts" in my last few years of working. I suddenly felt prompted to give this man my home phone number, and I asked how much his bike had cost. He said, "About 130 dollars at Walmart." I said, "You call me when you're better, and I'll get together with you and give you money for a new bike." I honestly didn't worry about giving my number to a stranger or about the fact he was homeless. Some call me naïve, but I call it "led by the Holy Spirit." Sometime later, I received a phone call from his brother, and we set a day he'd come in to my work. The ward clerk came and got me and said, "The man is here about the bike." There he was, sling on his arm, the same beautiful blue eyes, and with his brother. I gave him a check for more than the bike's cost, and he said, "Why are you doing this?" I said, "Because I care." He asked if I did this for all veterans, and I said, "No, you are special." He cried and said he didn't understand it. I just hugged him and his brother and wished him well. I can only hope, today, he's working and has shelter and warmth. I just wanted him to feel loved. I do love to pay for meals at breakfast or lunch out for veterans. It's fun not letting them know who did it.

We had a very young mother of a toddler in a coma with intractable seizures, and she was on life support. Her husband lived in our hospital room while other family members watched their baby. She was very, very ill, and he loved her so very much. We used to bring food to him. Another RN and I offered for him to come to our houses for a hot shower, at least. He declined. I had never invited a patient's family member to my home before. I'm not sure she did well; I can only pray for their future as a family.

One day, I had a young woman who had just delivered her baby while heavily intoxicated. The baby was born drunk and was up in the neonatal ICU, being watched closely. The mom was tearful, scared, and upset that she'd allowed this, now that her baby was suffering because of her actions. She was also shaky and probably in withdrawal. Her significant other looked dirty and unkempt and scared. Child Protective Services and our hospital NICU social worker both spoke with her and explained the baby would be removed from her and kept until she could prove she'd had rehab for drugs and alcohol. She cried and cried and said she wanted her baby back. I felt just as badly for the innocent baby like everyone else but, as the caregiver for the mom, saw her side of the story too. Yes, it was her wrong choice, her addiction, and her fault, but the baby would now be cared for, and she had some difficult choices to make. The comments and attitude from most of the other RNs, CPS, and the social worker were jaded toward her and the boyfriend. I know they see this a lot, but my heart saw an emotionally broken, physically ill, drug-damaged human. She'd been brought up short, now with a newborn in pain, all due to her epic failure as a mom. I kept encouraging her to get into rehab so she could get her baby back. Her boyfriend whispered to her that he had no money and was hungry. I went to my locker and only had a twenty-dollar bill. Another RN saw me give it to him and berated me for giving him "drug money." I said, "I believe he's hungry." He returned about twenty minutes later and gave me about fourteen dollars back. He'd gotten a drink, sandwich, and chips. We thanked each other, and my faith in my prompting to help was restored. It still breaks my heart that the treatment they got, and probably will continue to get, was not out of love; it was condemnation and judgment for their poor behavior. My heart breaks for that struggling baby, going through such a tough time at birth, but where are the caregivers who care enough to love on the broken, addicted, unbathed, lost ones? Is our resentment of the predicaments people place themselves in more than the love for a fellow human being in turmoil? I'm not a saint or sanctimonious; I just see the hurting on both sides. I suppose, if I worked in Child Protective Services, I would get hardened, too. I know I cannot fix everyone, only God can, but it's their choice. It's also the choice of *every* caregiver to open their heart enough to live in someone else's shoes for five minutes. I'm not saying we need to think like a drug addict or alcoholic but look at their brokenness and need for love. Wouldn't a little care and attempted understanding supersede the tired, resigned "they'll never get it" attitude of many caregivers?

Many other times, I went and got a book at the gift shop for a patient to read, flowers, cards, or money for cafeteria food. I even gave a warm bathrobe to a mother, who was a cardiac patient. I gave my beautiful Oakland Athletics jacket (I'd outgrown) to their baseball-loving son and a sweater to the dad. They didn't have warm clothes and were from outside our area. Mostly, I gave time. I often visited patients after they left ICU. I would go to the floor room they were in and sit and talk. I often asked if it was okay to have their address and have sent hundreds of "I care" cards post-hospitalization to patients and their families. Many, unfortunately, were sympathy cards. I still send Christmas cards to at least five or six patients. The satisfaction I got from times like these is far more than any paycheck.

They say nurses can't receive gifts. I never took money or anything expensive. It started with the toaster oven the priest I'd cared for in the Bay Area gave me as a wedding gift. In Mount Shasta, patients' families would bring in bags of homegrown veggies as thank-yous. They were greatly appreciated, as my husband was unemployed and I was making fourteen dollars an hour. We lived from paycheck to paycheck, never buying meat or anything at the supermarket unless it was on sale. We lived off our large garden and sometimes the food thankful families brought in. The guard at the inspection station near Interstate 5 also gave me the gift of a reassuring word and a feeling of safety on the snowy-night drive home alone on Interstate 5. A heart attack patient in Mount Shasta owned a gallery and sold photographs downtown. He was so grateful for my care he gave me a beautiful black-and-white photograph of two storm fronts coming from different directions together right over the top of Mount Shasta's peak. It's two swirling lenticular clouds twisting in opposite directions. I love it, and it's hanging in my home thirty-eight years later.

A Christmas cactus is now huge and flowers every Christmas on my patio. It came from a small piece of a cactus starter; I had rooted from one that a patient's husband gave to several other nurses and me over thirty years ago in our CCU. I think of him every time I marvel at its blooms.

The absolute, most glorious, memorable gift was that of life extended. The patient had an anterior MI (left ventricle) three days prior. He was asleep at nine p.m., and his rhythm suddenly deteriorated into a rapid, irregular ventricular tachycardia. He essentially was now dead, with a nonpumping heart, unless we changed that rhythm. My fellow RN and I jumped up and did what we were trained to do. One of us did a precordial thump, and one had gotten the crash cart and gave a shock (asynchronous defibrillation). He immediately went into sinus rhythm (normal) and started to arouse. He had no further issues, and he was so intensely grateful he gave about six of us dainty gold watches with "Thank you" engraved on the back. They could not be returned with engraving. I had worn mine until it didn't fit my wrist anymore and then gave it to my mom. Every subsequent Christmas or Thanksgiving, he would bring in a full dinner or candy or treats. He came every Christmas for twenty-one years until he knew no one anymore. The Lord had me be there for the last time he showed up to hug him. After all, if my fellow RN and I hadn't helped him all those years ago, he wouldn't have been there at all. I never took the credit. It's always about God. When it's your time to go, there is nothing our medical technology will do for you. God chose to let us intervene that night.

A grateful Samoan wife gave me a long turquoise handmade cotton muumuu once. I still wear it. I took care of a relative of an Olympic athlete once and met her dad, brother, and his wife. They were wonderful, sweet, open, caring people, and we got close. They gave me a very nice lotion set, but I missed meeting the athlete by one day. She flew in on my day off. To this day, I'd still love to meet her, not just because she's a great swimmer, but because if she's anything like the family I met, she's going to be wonderful.

One day I had a little white-haired lady in her nineties with a brain tumor causing some vision trouble. She had two or three other types of cancer, which had already been treated, and was still living alone. We grew close; she loved Jesus, and we talked about who we'd want to meet first in heaven. She and I were very open about death and what came after, having the hope of an eternity with God. Her daughter came to visit, and I really liked her. I tried to have an honest, open talk with them about how the lives of both of them were going to change, as now the mom couldn't live alone anymore, and the daughter would have to make time to help care for her. I related it to my own mom, who was chronically ill in assisted care. I even teared up as I said, "It can be hard as the daughter transitions to the caregiver and sometimes parent." I said it was

Debra Bauguess

hard on our relationship and for them just to love and cherish each other. I told the mom she would have to give up the independence and turn to her daughter, which my mom had done. (I had taken over as power of attorney.) They hugged and said they would. A short time later, the daughter came out, grabbed my hand, and pulled me into the room. The patient grabbed my other hand, and I knew something was up. They played an old Helen Reddy song, "You and Me against the World," about a beautiful mother-daughter relationship. I started crying as they both hugged me. My dying patient was ministering to me! I will never forget that feeling. I still have a picture on my phone the daughter took of her mom and me.

A gentleman came in with a debilitating stroke, and his wife had frantically driven one and a half hours to get there. She was distraught upon entering the room as she saw him. I'm sure they see a now helpless-looking, normally strong person, lying there disabled and semicomatose, and all the fears of a now altered, broken future come crashing down on them. I hugged her and started right in with caring and honesty. I answered questions and calmed her the best I could. She did calm down and started opening up about their life, and before she left for the night, she hugged me and said, "Your faith and calm manner helped me so much. Having a God-loving nurse made all the difference to me. I will not worry, now, tonight, knowing whose hands he's in." She had a strong faith in the Lord also. The next day she gave me a beautiful crystal rock she'd found to always remind me of them. It still sits on my dresser.

I admitted a young pastor with a brain bleed. He was awake but paralyzed on one side. He was in our ICU for about thirty-five days. I took care of him a lot and grew very close to his wife and parents. He and his wife loved each other so very much. She lived in the room with him and rarely left. One night, his wife started crying because her washing machine had broken and she didn't have time or the money (she wasn't working while staying with him) to fix it. As I listened to her, a friend of theirs came to visit. He'd been addicted and homeless, and he'd seen the pastor patient preach at Union Gospel Mission downtown. This visitor had turned to Jesus because of my patient's sermon. He heard the wife's washing machine story and said he had to go. He left and came back a couple of hours later and, without saying a word, placed a roll of something in the wife's hand. He left again, and she came out crying, "Debbie, look what he did." The visitor, who'd been homeless and was now saved, had put 500 dollars in the wife's hand for a new machine. It probably was his life savings, as he worked at Union Gospel for minimum wage. Something broke inside me, like a dam breaking. I wanted to give like that. The patient had a rocky course and left our ICU only to come back with blood clots in his lungs. He recovered from that and left our unit again and was one day away from leaving for rehab when he rebled in his brain and came back in, now brain-dead. I went to his funeral and reception and graveside ceremony and was treated like family. My life changed after meeting them. I'm now a giver and build up my treasures in heaven.

One morning, a very beautiful young man in his twenties came in semiconscious, having a recent history of going unconscious on the treadmill at a gym. He was young and healthy in every other respect. As I tried to settle him, his parents came in and sat in a corner, looking scared. I noticed immediately his breathing was not normal and drew on years of experience and called the MD and respiratory therapist to come to intubate him. His ability to breathe effectively was deteriorating rapidly. He was moaning, gasping, diaphoretic and obtunded. I assured the parents I knew what I was doing; I'd been an RN for over forty years. I had them wait in the waiting room so we could intubate him and then whisked him off for a CT of his brain. He, unfortunately, had a small bleed in an area of the midbrain, where you never "wake up" again. I don't believe they ever figured out an actual reason, as he was a health nut with no history of anything that would hurt his body. I grew very close to his sister, girlfriend, mom, dad, and other visiting relatives. I took care of him a lot in the next two or three weeks that he was in our unit. If I had a different assignment, I'd still spend time talking with and comforting the family when I could. They had faith also, which always brings hope. When he graduated to another floor, after ICU, I would go up on breaks and after work to spend time with them. They were grieving so over a very young life drastically altered. I desperately wanted to comfort and help. During this time, unbeknownst to me, they each had separately written a letter of thanks and commendation about me and our unit's caring to our CEO. I was going through a tough time with a complaint an MD had made about me, and when I was feeling most alone and in need of strength, these two notes were sent to me by my critical-care nurse director. The timing of an unexpected, uplifting word of thanks from a grateful family I deeply cared about couldn't have come at a moment I needed it more. Before he left our hospital to go to a facility in the LA area for long-term care (now eyes open and able to make some facial movement but no actual speech), they gave me a furry cat blanket. The patient and I both loved cats. It sits on top of me as I write this. I still correspond with his mom.

In my last few months at work, I had a mother of several daughters come in with a severe brain bleed. I believe it was a subarachnoid hemorrhage. She was comatose with a grievous injury. I was extremely busy with her as she kept showing increasing signs of worsening. Thank You, Jesus: my years of experience kicked in, and I saw the subtle changes of a rapidly swelling brain. She was more deeply comatose; her EVD (external ventricular drain) quit draining, meaning the ventricle inside the brain, normally full of fluid, was "squished" closed by increasing brain tissues swelling from rising pressure. Her pupils became moderately unequal, also reflecting increased intracranial pressure. I quickly told the three God-believing daughters to rouse everyone and pray and called the MD emergently. It was around 6:30 at night on a holiday Sunday. The on-call neuro intensivist was at home, and the only neurosurgeon was occupied in an elective surgery. Our robot cruised down the hall to my room, and I could show the MD on the screen the patient's EVD and neuro signs. He came in immediately. I was already telling the family that she'd need emergency brain surgery to relieve pressure (craniectomy, or skull-flap removal). First, there was no available neurosurgeon, and second, it was a Sunday and holiday time. The MD called for quite some time, I think about nine people, to find a downtown neurosurgeon who was willing to come in. This was miracle number one. Then the next problem was that this MD had no privileges at our hospital, and the administrator on call had to be gotten ahold of to give them. This was miracle number two. The next problem was that it would take him over one hour to get there. We didn't think the mom would make it that long. She had slowly worsening vital signs. The surgeon walked in about fifteen minutes later: miracle number three. Next, we needed an OR for emergency surgery, and there were none and no OR crew to do it. I had the family updated and kept asking them to pray hard. They were in the waiting room. As I sat down to give the night-shift report, the OR crew walked through our doors and said, "We're here to take her; we're ready!" Miracle number four had just happened after all the prayer. I was crying; the night RN was amazed; the daughters and husband were crying. I found out through subsequent phone calls on my days off that she had survived. One daughter gave me a gift of a listening, caring angel who sits on a table in my living room. Another daughter gave me an angel ornament that says, "Nurses are angels with invisible wings," and it hangs on my lamp next to me. I will always treasure these heartfelt mementos from people who felt the love I gave. It made my career all worthwhile. It was in the giving that I received (Saint Francis of Assisi). The gifts were not necessary but loved all the same because I can look at them now and see a life I touched.

> *"In everything I did, I showed you that by this kind of hard work we must help the weak, remembering the words the Lord Jesus himself said: 'It is more blessed to give than to receive.'"*
>
> — Acts 20:35

TEACHING MOMENT

What you *get* back when you *give* far outweighs how much or what you gave. It lets the patient know they matter and you care. Only give what you want to or feel prompted to give. Giving is not always about money: you can give effort, time, empathy, a shoulder to cry on, etc. Receiving is deeply humbling and harder for some of us. Just be grateful you impacted another's life to the point that they want to show you how much you meant to them.

THE POWER OF A HUG

Hugs, in place of words, are powerful. I always hugged people, especially when I didn't know what to say, or the emotion was grief, devastation, or joy and gratitude. I know many people are not touchy-feely or huggers, but unabashedly, I am and will always be. A hug given in ICU is as if you are a life raft in the middle of raging seas, and the patient or family hangs on for dear life. You are needed so that they don't sink. A young nurse in my unit was newly pregnant and happy to tell me "something was baking in the oven." A few weeks later, I noticed she was very quiet. I asked if she was okay, and she told me she'd lost the baby and wasn't really telling anyone. I hugged her and held her while she cried a little. I told her it was okay to cry and not hold it in. I assured her I cared and loved her and would be there for her if she needed to talk. I gave her a pendant saying, "I will hold you in my heart until I can hold you in my arms in heaven." Every day we worked together from that day on, we found each other and hugged. Our day was not okay if we did not. I always tried to encourage her to grieve the loss and cherish her other two kids at home. I grew to think of her as a younger sister and love her sweet, caring spirit. She made me a gift and wrote a beautiful card when I retired, saying I was the only one who made her feel it was okay to mourn her loss. I will always love her.

Years ago, in our eleven-bed CCU, my patient was a young Russian girl who was in a vegetative coma (as well as her baby, taken by C-section in ER). Her heart had stopped, and now the never-to-awaken young mom was in our unit for about the second or third week. I had taken care of her a lot. Just outside her room, a woman was sobbing as though her heart would break, with her face in her hands. I looked around to see if anyone else saw her. She was alone. I stepped out and just grabbed her and held her close for many minutes while she cried and cried. Finally, she stepped back and said, "You will never know what that meant." She said she'd just been given the news that her mother was worse (a patient in our unit) and then received a phone call that her brother had just fallen off a building and landed on his head and might be brain-dead at a downtown hospital. We hugged again, and still total strangers, each knew we'd impacted each other's lives. She thanked me over and over and offered a free service to me at her salon if I ever needed it. I never saw her again.

A few days later, as multiple deacons and pastors came in to pray over the Russian girl, it got loud, and I gently shut the glass doors. I then went to the adjacent patient room to close their doors due to the loud prayers. I explained they were praying due to a sad situation next door. The patient's wife, sitting across the room, said, "Are you okay?" Something must have shown on my face. I said, "I'm okay; it's just been a sad day." She said, "I don't think you are okay," and got up and came over and grabbed me and hugged the stuffing out of me as her husband watched. I started sobbing as her caring seeped in. I let go of all the horror and sadness next door. After a short time, I tried to step back, and she said, "You're not done yet." She grabbed me again and hugged me hard until I truly felt better. We never exchanged names; it was a God-given payback from one stranger to another for the same mercy shown a few days before. I will *never* forget either of those hugs.

One night, my older stroke patient was about to be transferred to another major nearby hospital because she was now stable and insurance dictated it. She was very debilitated and probably never going to get home. Her significant other got angry and said, "They'll kill her over there; we've been there before. I won't let her go there." He got on his phone, called the other hospital, and loudly argued with the transfer coordinator. He was crying, and his face was really red. I could hear the coordinator yelling back at him on his phone, saying that if they denied the transfer, he would have to pay her bill (which, of course, they could not). My charge RN was sitting five feet away, covering a break for my neighbor nurse. He was watching the tantrum carefully for possible escalation to violence, something we were frequently exposed to. The gentleman finally said, "I guess you have to take her, but I'm not happy about it." He hung up, and his face was flushed, and he was breathing heavily and crying. He looked utterly forlorn and lost. I jumped up, grabbed him, and hugged him. For a split second, I thought, *Wow, he's tall and big and angry. Was this wise?* He started crying harder, grabbed me back, and held on for minutes while he sobbed. He told me, "Thank you for your caring," over and over. I looked half in amazement myself at my charge RN, and he just said, "Wow! I didn't see that coming." I knew that hug in his desperate moment defused his anger. It stopped him in his tracks.

One day, as I sat in an early a.m. report, I saw a tiny Spanish older woman come in to visit her very ill son down the hall. I'd seen her before, and she came every day. I jumped up and stood in front of her and opened my arms; she melted into me and cried and hugged me back so hard. I knew very little Spanish, and she knew very little English, but no words were needed. I continued getting the report, and she went to see her son. She knew I cared. From that day on, for the next couple of weeks, when I was on, every time she walked through our doors and saw me, she tapped my shoulder and stood there with her arms out. We hugged, kissed each other's cheeks, and got teary each time. She would even stand behind me until I was finished with the report before hugging me. It's true: *hugs born of love transcend language.*

Sometimes, I would have a few extra minutes where I was caught up and my two patients were stable and asleep. Instead of sitting, I would walk up the hallway and pray and look in rooms for someone who looked forlorn. That day, I saw a wife in a recliner across the room, looking very sad, while her comatose husband lay in bed on a ventilator. I knew he wasn't going to live long, and I said, "I know you don't know me, but you look like you need a hug." She got up and said, "I'll probably cry." I said, "That is okay; I might, too." We hugged and hugged, and she cried, and then I sat beside her and listened to what she was going through. We hugged again, and I went back to my patients. The next day, my assignment was in our other hallway, away from her husband's room. About halfway through the shift, a young RN coworker came over and said, "Deb, will you come over and hug my patient's wife? She asked for the girl who hugged her yesterday. Her husband's a DNR and dying right now, and you know I don't hug." I remembered her and went right over and was hugging her tightly as her husband's heart rate slowed and stopped. What are the odds of me picking her to hug the day before and now to be holding her at the exact moment her husband died a day later? She spent about ten minutes telling me about their love, life, and marriage and told me he was the best man she'd ever known.

Debra Bauguess

Then she said, "Okay, I'm ready now," and got ready to leave. We hugged once more, never knowing names and never seeing each other again. Her husband's nurse at least knew to come to get me; God bless him.

On one of my last days at work, as I cared for a man with a probable life-altering stroke, his wife came outside the room and sat next to me. We both had masks on due to COVID-19, had good health, and were without fever. She started to cry as I asked how she was dealing with her husband's stroke. She proceeded to tell me all she was going through. It was really quite overwhelming, as she'd recently lost someone she loved and had multiple other crises happening. She was in obvious pain, and I reached for her and hugged her while she sobbed on my shoulder. Another nurse walked by and said I was "naïve" and should know better. Covid or no Covid rules, we were both masked and healthy, and the wife and I received the blessing only caring, grieving hearts can share. I followed my God's prompting and wrapped my arms around a suffering human being. I see the big picture at times like that and *know* I did the only loving, right thing. I truly feel sorry for all those who I could, and I wish I would, reach out and comfort, those who are hurting, right when they need it most.

Hugs are free, easy, and they cross the barrier of culture, language, and words to convey caring and love in a moment of great need. I will never change who I am or what I am and vow to hug anyone who needs it until my dying day. I like to think that all the love of Jesus is flowing through me to them and wraps them, just for a moment in time, in a blanket of love, as they've never felt before. A hug doesn't fix the illness or change the circumstances, but it transfers pure, unadulterated love from one heart to another. Many times, I saw a stranger walking away from a very ill loved one's room in shock, and I would ask their permission to hug them. No one ever said no. To this day, people call me the hugging nurse. My bird-feed store guy waits for a hug every time I go there now because he had once teared up, talking about his wife who had died, and I had hugged him. You do not know what a hug means until you truly need one.

Love must be sincere. Hate what is evil; cling to what is good. Be devoted to one another in love. Honor one another above yourselves. Never be lacking in zeal, but keep your spiritual fervor, serving the LORD. Be joyful in hope, patient in affliction, and faithful in prayer. Share with God's people who are in need. Practice hospitality.

— Romans 12:9–13

TEACHING MOMENT

Many people aren't huggers (staff and patients). Find other ways to convey deep caring. Sometimes words alone are not enough. Find where you are comfortable and practice some form of touch. Ninety-nine percent of hurting patients and families crave the human touch for comfort. It can be very simple: just touch a shoulder, hand, or wipe a face with a wash-cloth.

THE ONES YOU
NEVER FORGET

This chapter is a collage of moments that forever altered my viewpoint on the resilience of the human race.

D. P. was an elderly gentleman who came in many, many times with ventricular tachycardia. He would have a fast pulse and would be in CHF (congestive heart failure). His lungs would be full of fluid that the heart could not pump out effectively. We started using the new drug, amiodarone, on him, which led to pneumonia. I would spend hours talking with him. He was giving and wise and caring. I got very close to his daughter and son. His was the first funeral I ever went to.

F. W. was a skinny little old Black man with a heart of gold. He was a veteran. He had diabetes and quite severe peripheral arterial and venous disease, especially in his lower extremities. I took care of him many times as he got weaker, lost weight, and lost limbs due to gangrene. He never stopped opening his garage to children on his street who were bored and needed a friend. He tinkered and would teach these kids they were important and how to fix things like toasters and appliances. He used to fix all his neighbors' broken machines for free. We used to write cards to each other. I miss his sweet nature.

I became humbled by an Indian woman with severe heart disease; upon finding out, she had started the feeding program for the poor in Calcutta, India. She had worked alongside Mother Teresa and fed millions of people. How does one live up to that? Hers was the second funeral I attended. I got close to her kids.

In Mount Shasta, a twentyish-year-old woman rolled her VW Beetle at night to avoid hitting a cat on a mountain road. I admitted her, and she had broken almost every major bone in her body: clavicle, pelvis, ribs, arms, legs, and had internal bleeding. It was a life-and-death fight to stabilize her. We gave countless liters of fluid and many units of blood, and she had multiple surgeries. We were cleaning grass, asphalt, and broken glass out of her hair and wounds for days. She was in our ICU for a long time and then out on the medical floor for a couple of months. She had the most sweet, positive attitude I think I've ever seen. One day, we pushed her bed outside the hospital into bright sunshine with a full-on view of Mount Shasta. We let her bask in the sun and wind and hear the birds. Much later, she walked out of our hospital, and I later heard she was back at her favorite hobby, dancing.

D. E. was a fellow RN educator and friend. He had a loving family, and his patients loved his manner. I adored him. He came to work and was at the bedside when he suddenly didn't feel well and dropped to the floor. His beloved coworkers, friends, and MDs tried desperately to save him, but it was his time. Many fellow care workers were traumatized by "coding" him. They had counselors in the hospital to help. I thank him for the role he played in my love for teaching.

A nice young red-haired woman came in with shortness of breath, was pale, and had low blood pressure. She was deteriorating fast. We determined she had cardiac tamponade and had to do an emergency pericardiocentesis. She had fluid around her heart inside the sack that contains the heart, and it kept the heart from pumping well; the procedure drains the fluid out. We later discovered her pericardial effusion (fluid around her heart) was from cancer, and she died a short time later. When years later, I admitted the next young woman with sudden cardiac tamponade, I told the MD to check for cancer, and I was right. I found that several other young patients with sudden, unexplained, pericardial effusions and cardiac tamponade all had cancer when they came in with these same symptoms. Again, I remember how scared she was, but how brave and grace-filled she was about her diagnosis.

I took care of a beautiful young woman who needed a heart transplant and was on the transplant list. She and her boyfriend wanted to marry and go on a honeymoon. He cherished her so much. After multiple admits and a weakening heart, she still was not closer to knowing if or when a heart would be available. They decided to marry and go on a honeymoon, not knowing how much time they had left. They left the state, had the wedding and trip of their dreams, and she was removed from the top of the transplant list to the bottom, as she'd left the state and broken their rules. They had known this would happen but wanted a glorious time of sharing their love together before her time ran out. She died shortly thereafter, and her husband came to thank us for the love we had showered on them. I've never met a young man as dedicated and self-sacrificing as him. He impressed all of us mightily, as did she, with their spunk, sweet spirit, and love for life.

I took care of a thirtyish-year-old man with one leg missing. As we got to know each other, I asked how he'd lost it. He very cockily said, "I was spearfishing, had a fish on the end of my spear, and a shark came along. The shark wanted *my* fish, and I didn't want him to have it, so the shark took my leg." Wow! Somehow I think I would have deferred to the shark.

A man in his fifties with several grown children needed a heart transplant and was on an intra-aortic balloon pump. This portable machine eases the workload on a stressed, failing heart. Your own heart has to pump; the machine just makes the pumping a little easier and buys time to get to transplant or heart surgery. He and his family were hardworking, honest, gracious people. He'd never gotten his green card, though he'd worked in our country for many years. He was on this temporary piece of lifesaving equipment, and after much deliberation, the state turned him down for the 1.5 million dollar surgery he would need because he wasn't a citizen. He accepted it, but his children and we had a much harder time with that decision. How and who our government decides to save is on them; I do not want to be there when they are judged someday. In today's time, they are putting illegal immigrants in housing, paying for healthcare and schooling. Our patient had paid taxes and worked hard in this country he loved for many years. I'll never forget the anguish the family and we felt when we had to turn the life-support machine off and watch him fade away. I'll always see his loving eyes focused on his children, for the rest of my life.

One p.m., the medical chief of staff came in with cardiac tamponade and was dying. The cardiologist said, "Let's tap him quickly" (pericardiocentesis). I had never done this procedure before, and the other RN was pregnant and couldn't help because we had fluoroscopy in the room (X-ray equipment). I took a big breath and told the MD I'd never done one but for him to talk me through it and I would do my best to help him. It worked, but the chief of staff kept trying to die, and the MD had to go in the back of an ambulance with him downtown to a sister hospital that did open-heart surgery because his heart kept trying to stop. The next day in the paper, I saw an article that praised two teenagers for finding him slumped over on a city street. They had called 911. No mention was ever made about the two people who saved his life inside the hospital. The nursing care and MD procedures that saved lives were never appreciated by anyone but the patient and their family, which is all we need. Seeing someone keep living after a near-death experience was all I ever needed to see to feel reward and have the strength to keep doing it.

I had the honor of caring for a fellow RN's mother. She was about the cutest, nicest little lady I'd ever met, and I fell in love with her and her husband immediately. They'd been married for many years. The RN's mom deteriorated and was in severe crisis with failing lungs and was on a ventilator (breathing machine). She needed sedation just to help the machine be able to get air into her noncompliant lungs. Normal lung tissue is compliant and stretches and moves easily, but sick lungs are noncompliant and can get stiff, and they do not fill with air easily (you have to push oxygen in with force). I'll never forget the husband saying he wanted to lighten the sedation just to see her eyes open and look at him one more time. My heart broke, as I had to tell him she'd suffer. Less sedation would affect her ability to get oxygen and breathe, and she would panic. He understood, but as I held him, I grieved with him. I couldn't imagine not seeing my love of many years look at me again before we turned off life support.

One of my dear young fellow RNs came back from a break, and her boyfriend was hiding in an empty room with a ring. We all watched on a patient's room video camera while he proposed to our friend. Of course, she accepted. They had a beautiful fairytale wedding in the Napa Valley and a dream honeymoon in Italy, and about a year and a half later, I heard he'd died. Life is not fair, but she did have a son by him to raise and love. I was shocked to hear the news from an MD at work one day and burst into tears. Life is so very precious. She moved out of the area but, last I heard, was doing very well and had a wonderful little boy who she adored.

We had a suicidal patient in a corner room, awaiting transfer to a mental health facility for treatment. Everything of potential harm had been removed from her room. Somehow a plastic pencil got into her hands, and she started stabbing her neck. I had visions of her hitting her carotid artery and dying in front of us, with blood flying everywhere. A security guard helped calm her down with seemingly magical powers, and I told him, "You're not just a security guard, are you?" He said he was a pastor in a nearby church and had a heart for the broken and lost. We kept a friendship after that; he was so inspiring. Every time we saw each other, we hugged. Last I heard, he had high-blood-pressure problems and could not work as a security guard any longer. I know his heart was for the lost and broken, though, and he was trying to start up a church to pastor them.

I admitted a patient having a stroke and a myocardial infarction at the same time. As I garnered the details, he said he'd had both a stroke and MI before. He'd recovered, gone home, and continued to smoke. He told me this and then grinned at me. This time he felt chest pain (the same kind as his previous heart attack) and got in a car to drive himself to the hospital. He got to the hospital, still having chest pain, and decided to smoke a quick cigarette, as we didn't allow smoking inside. It gave him another stroke while he was sitting in his car. I don't know how he got inside the ER doors, but he got help and actually survived again. I marveled at him for his seeming "death wish." He laughed and was happy to have beaten the odds again and thought the whole thing was a lark. I truly do not understand some people. They are so cavalier about dying and the risks they are taking when so many others would give anything to have one more day on this planet.

One night, at a prayer-group meeting at my church, a young pastor came over to me, laid his hands on my head, and said, "Tomorrow morning, very early, you will lay hands on someone and have a direct impact on saving their life." He didn't know I was an ICU RN and dealt with this kind of thing daily. The next a.m. at work, at about 07:15 a.m., I was helping the neuro critical-care intensivist place an EVD into a patient's brain. She was an RN and had a subarachnoid hemorrhage in her brain, causing swelling and high pressures, necessitating the drain. Her heart stopped, and I tried to do a few chest compressions with her upright in the bed. I called a code blue and for a crash cart, and the doctor said, "I'm not going to stop what I'm doing." I said, "Yes, you are, sir, because her heart has stopped and we're about to do CPR." After a few moments, her rhythm spontaneously returned; the MD placed his line and then wanted to send her for a lengthy procedure in the neuroradiology suite. I begged him to call a cardiologist first to place a temporary pacemaker, as this was the second time her heart had stopped in twenty-four hours, and that situation needed to be fixed first. He agreed, and she got the pacer and the neuro procedure. While she was being cared for, I sat the husband down and told him about what had been said to me at church. I also told him how I sit in my car every morning before work and pray for the exact assignment God needs me to be in. He was shocked and amazed at how things had played out and so very grateful. After a long recovery, she went home. They walked back in to see me several months later, and what a miracle: she was completely fine. We all three hugged and hugged, marveling at the connectedness of different lives and the timing involved in how everything had played out. I truly felt I was meant to be her nurse that day.

In Mount Shasta, I had a man who was a severe alcoholic and had not felt well and had driven himself to the hospital. He was found unconscious in his car and was subsequently found to have a leaking aortic aneurysm, requiring immediate emergency surgery. His recovery in our ICU was horrendous. He was very unstable overall after such a major surgery but then went into full-blown DTs (acute alcohol withdrawal). He hit, kicked, bit, and screamed for days. My fellow RN got bitten on her shoulder by him and got a funny look on her face, turned around, and walked out of the hospital, never to return. This man remained in our hospital for many weeks with everyone involved, scrambling to help him stay alive and stable. We "fixed" him, got him through DTs, and I read, to my dismay, about two or three months later, that he'd gotten drunk and fallen down the basement stairs at home, broken his neck, and died. So much for our lifesaving and fixing abilities. Too many patients go right back to what they are comfortable with (good or bad) after all our help.

We frequently had prisoners shackled to the bed, some from Folsom Prison and some just from a local county jail with nonviolent offenses. One or two guards would have to sit in their room twenty-four hours a day. This Black fellow was sweet; I really liked him immediately. He'd had a stroke and was weak on one side but luckier than most, although he'd been living in his car, homeless in Fairfield. I got to talking with the patient about what led him to this place in his life. He was in jail for a nonviolent offense. He proceeded to tell me of his dream to cook, his memories in the kitchen with his grandma, and about his brother who had been killed. He had dreams, great loss, and now, even in this situation, hope for a better life. I spent time and care on him and, at my shift's end, placed my hand on his heart and said, "I see a good man in there; you have hope in humanity and dreams to fill and past family love to hold you up. I care about your future and you and will pray for you." I gave him a Union Gospel card to try and get off the streets (they take in homeless, addicted men in Sacramento and help them and lead them to God). He had faith in God, and I went out of my way to encourage him to get healthy and find a job and a place to stay. The guard got a little upset when I touched the patient but let me after he saw how it was affecting the patient. He was tearing up. When I left, he handed me a paper towel he'd written on with a black marker. It said, "I've never seen such unconditional love. As I watched, all day, the many people going to and fro outside this door, you chose to keep coming in and asking about my life and pouring into me love and some of your life. It meant the world to me. I want to turn my life around because of you. Thank you." That note is still in my Bible today. It means so very much to me. I was so upset because the system did not want to spend more money on him for rehab, so it commuted his leftover jail time and sent him back out onto the streets with a walker and a limp and a weak arm. I pray he sought help because our state did not want to help him and sent him back to his original circumstances in a worse condition than before. These were the hardest people to let go of; I worry and pray so hard for them because it doesn't seem like our country and state are out to help the helpless or truly needy, much of the time. They see them as repeat offenders or hopelessly stuck instead of wonderful human beings with hopes and dreams just as they have in their own lives.

My most inspiring patient is last. She came in with a severe stroke. She was exercising in a gym, and a strong elastic band snapped and hit her in the side of the neck. Other than bruising and soreness, she did well for a short time and then got weak on one side. She'd traumatized her carotid artery, and a blood clot had broken off and went up into her brain, causing a large stroke. She was paralyzed on one side and on life support. She was young, with kids and a very supportive husband. She fought back hard to survive and did. She'd had a piece of skull removed because her brain was so swollen. She went to rehab with a helmet to protect her brain. She needed time to heal and have her brain shrink back to normal size. About six months later, I had the privilege to care for her again. She was in to have the piece of removed skull put back into place. She told me, "Debbie, I have half a brain, and I'm going to run half a marathon." Half her brain was affected, and she had difficulty walking and couldn't use one arm. She was an RN and no longer working. She later sent me a picture of her "running" in the half marathon (more like a fast walk). I had it up on our breakroom wall for a long time. She also returned to school, got her master's in counseling, and now helps people in various tragic, life-altering situations. She had told me, "There are respiratory therapists, physical therapists, occupational therapists, and speech therapists but no emotional therapists. That's what I want to do." She did! We still correspond, and I sent flowers to her house for her arrival home after her second brain surgery.

She has since helped me with two of my patients with devastating strokes. I will always be inspired by her: *she is my hero.*

One day, I received a patient from the cardiac-catheterization lab, and they had placed an intra-aortic balloon pump in him to help his failing heart. He was still doing poorly and in obvious cardiogenic shock after I received him in my unit. I immediately called his MD, now back in the office, and explained to him that the patient was worsening and that I'd discovered he had the wrong-sized balloon inside him, so it wasn't helping him. I gave him some other information and said he needed to come back over and replace the balloon with a larger one. He said he would later, after office hours. I said, "No, sir, you need to be here in ten minutes or less; this is absolutely emergent." I knew this because of my thirty-plus years' experience in coronary care ICU and my four and a half years teaching the intra-aortic balloon pump for Arrow on the West Coast of California. He was there fast; the procedure was done, and the patient was somewhat more stable. The MD left. The next day, the MD said, "Debbie, what did you mean when you said I had to come now because…" I said, "You didn't understand what I was saying?" He said, "Not entirely." I said, "Why did you come over so fast, then?" He said, "Because you told me to." We both hugged, and I cried.

To this day, I have never felt such unconditional trust and respect from someone as from Dr. B. He used to call me "Daybee." He followed me down a fifth-floor stairwell late one night as I left shift to beg me to stay and help him with an intra-aortic balloon pump insertion. The nurse helping him wasn't as familiar with it yet (though soon became an expert). I returned to help after thirteen long hours already because I loved him and wanted to help him. He and I are both retired, but he's my favorite. This event, where he came in because I told him to earned me the Daisy Award (a special award for healthcare people doing extraordinary things). I cherish the honor from my manager, and the pin is still on my name tag.

These stories are all true and are all about human beings who chose to play a role in their health, whether good or bad. We want the best for our patients and pray our hard work pays off and that they are concerned enough to take better care of themselves once home. I will never, ever forget any of these and many more, too many to count. I probably laid hands on thousands of patients and hugged countless family members. Every single person, though, left a mark on me and became part of my life. They *all* taught me something, mostly about courage, resiliency, and love.

> *"God is not unjust; he will not forget your work and the love you have shown him as you have helped his people and continue to help them."*
>
> — Hebrews 6:10

> *"For it is God who works in you to will and to act in order to fulfill his good purpose."*
>
> — Philippians 2:13

TEACHING MOMENT

You will all have some who you never forget. Whether painful or joyful, those memories become a part of who you develop

Debra Bauguess

into as a caregiver. Know that you were given a very special glimpse into an extraordinary human's life for a reason. Cherish each memory.

MIRACLES AND TRAGEDIES

A tragedy can so easily become a miracle and vice versa. When you see a truly supernatural event, it lets you know there are forces outside our visible realm in control of our destinies.

There is a two-lane road that goes from Interstate 5 to a small town named McCloud, southeast of Mount Shasta. It's narrow, mountainous, and isolated. One night, a man pulled over onto a large, wide turnout to change a flat tire. He was well off the road, without another car for miles. A man had a heart attack at the wheel while driving and slumped over, and his moving vehicle veered off the rarely traveled road and swerved into my patient. The odds are astronomical of that even happening. My patient was severely injured with a crushed leg as his major injury. We were lucky to have an excellent orthopedic surgeon at Mount Shasta Hospital. He spent hours in the operating room, pinning and screwing this man's multiple small pieces of bone back together in his leg. I recovered him in my ICU, and he had a large cagelike contraption around his entire leg, called an external fixation device. He spent a long time in the ICU and in the hospital, with physical therapy. I last saw him in his place of business, doing well. He was a sweet, gentle, caring man, and I loved him. He never gave up hope or faith in us or the fact that he *would* walk again.

I had a young man who had a .22 rifle shot injury that I recovered. His dad saw him come home from work late one night around midnight and, in his drunken stupor, thought he was the next-door neighbor who he hated. He pulled out his .22 rifle and shot his own son. The patient was in our ICU for a long time; we fixed the initial injury, which was grievous, but it took longer to discover that the source of his continued bleeding was a fragment of a bullet that had ricocheted off a rib and nicked his kidney. They did one final surgery; we gave blood, and he did well and forgave his dad. I always wondered if the dad got help or the son moved out. This young man was smart, kind, and as nice as he could be; I hope he became something really special. I always told patients who recovered from great injuries that the Lord had a reason for their survival and to change what they could with their second chance at life.

My elderly female patient had a devastating left middle cerebral artery stroke that severely affected her ability to talk. The hard thing was (which happened all too much) that she was the caregiver for her frail husband at home. It was never one issue to deal with, and it broke our hearts and made the care, which includes the entire family, so much more compli-cated. All she could say was, "Ka, ka, ka, ka." I tried for an hour with numbers, vowels, and simple words, and she could not say it, though she understood me and would try to say them. Her son said she used to be in a church choir, so I tried singing. Music and singing come from a different location in the brain than language and words. I started singing "Amazing Grace," and she eased back in her chair, head relaxed against the back, opened her mouth, and sang "Amazing Grace" with easily recognizable words. We developed a crowd. Her son and many team members, all in awe, stood outside her door and listened while she sang "How Great Thou Art" and "Amazing Grace" again. Memories and great loves (like hymns) are strong mo-tivators. A few of us were tearing up (I always do when in the

Debra Bauguess

face of something so heart-clenching). The two sons had much to deal with because now, they had two ill parents to care for, but I have to hope it all worked out. I doubt that that lady's ability to speak ever came back.

In Mount Shasta, I recovered a young woman who'd left her child with her mom to raise while she became transient and floated from town to town, getting high and drunk. She was in Dunsmuir, jumping on and off moving trains, high on drugs. She fell underneath the moving wheels. She lost both legs above the knees. I thought limbs could be reattached, but the pictures reflected why hers could not be. The train wheels are wide, and there was so much grit, tar, dirt, oil, and rock involved that there were no clean margins on either end of leg or limb to reattach to. Upon seeing those pictures of the injury, I felt nauseous. She was very ill and had lost a lot of blood. As she woke up in recovery, her first words were, "Are they gone?" I gently said, "Yes, both your legs are gone; I'm so very sorry." She said, "I can handle it!" She turned her head away from me, closed her eyes, and dismissed me. Shortly thereafter, she used to wheel around the halls in her wheelchair, back and forth, never staying in her room. She got a free wheelchair from the hospital and then tried to sue the railroad, as, after all, it was *their* fault. I assume the rest of her life continued in the same manner. At least her child was, hopefully, raised in love by the grandmother. She never once cried, grieved, or said thank-you to anyone; she had that "chip on her shoulder," and we "owed" her. It still truly amazes me how some people with attitudes like hers get through life.

When I prayed in my car before work, I asked God to place me in specific moments of need for specific patients. I went into a fellow nurse's room to help her get a new admit settled.

It was a young woman with a stroke, and half her body was paralyzed. She had just been helicoptered in by Life Flight to us. She looked terrified. I said, "Are you scared?" She grabbed my hand with her one good hand and said, "Oh yes." I said, "Do you have faith or believe in God?" She said, "Oh yes, I love Jesus." I told her I did too, and we both hugged and teared up. I asked if she wanted me to pray for her, and she did. I prayed, and she started half laughing and half crying and said it was answered prayer. In the helicopter, on the way there, she'd asked for someone who knew God to walk through the door on her arrival and comfort her. When the admitting RN asked if we knew each other, the patient said, "We are sisters." I got the oddest look from her RN because the patient was dark-skinned and I was light-skinned. The patient and I just kept holding hands, and I reassured her as much as possible to hold on to her faith to get through this. I pray she got some strength back on her paralyzed side.

Another day, in a different ICU, I went into another RN's room upon seeing a distraught-looking husband watching his elderly wife get admitted. I said, "Are you okay?" He said, "No. Do you know the Holy Spirit?" I said that I did and sat down, as he asked if I would pray with him. We prayed together, and he told me he had just asked God to send someone through the door who knew the Holy Spirit who would pray with him. These times would knock my socks off as I would go home realizing the Lord has all things timed and perfectly arranged to connect His people. Our part of the story is that we ask for help to find these people who *need* us.

As I started in a new church, I decided to go up to the altar to be prayed for. I asked for strength to keep making the right choices as I had just come through a tough time in my

Debra Bauguess

life. One of the women said, "You've come out of Egypt; don't go back." Many years later, I had a Russian pastor as a patient. He loved God, and we were talking about the Lord. Suddenly he grabbed my hand and said, "I'm going to pray for you now." He prayed in his prayer language (it was not Russian), and I heard the word "Egypt." Afterward, I asked if he knew what he'd said. He said, "Of course not; it was the Holy Spirit." I said that I understood that but heard the word "Egypt." He looked right at me and said, "You've come out of Egypt; don't go back." Wow! This was confirmation of the Lord's hand on my life years apart from two total strangers.

One day, I admitted a lovely elderly woman who had felt suddenly faint with strokelike symptoms in a furniture store. The young employee at the store recognized the signs and called 911 immediately. She made it to our Northern California comprehensive stroke center in record time and got a clot dissolver (tPA) and an immediate thrombectomy where they go to interventional neuroradiology and get the blood clot taken out of the brain artery closed by it with a special device. She was completely back to normal, thanking God for her miraculous recovery. There is a three-hour "window" to get stroke victims into a stroke center before irreversible damage happens, at least with a blood-clot stroke (embolic stroke). This thrombectomy procedure can be tried within a longer time frame, but you still run the risk of damage to the unoxygenated area being irreversible.

When I was CCU supervisor (for about fifteen years), I went to every single code blue in the hospital when I worked. One code was a young mom just after a C-section. She'd had a healthy baby but was still on the OR table, "bleeding out." Another ICU RN and I went, and for over two hours, CPR was done on her while we overhead paged, "Any surgeon in the house, please come to OR." We hung over forty units of blood as fast as we could and kept doing good CPR as multiple surgeons looked for her source of bleeding. Amazingly, it was a cardiac surgeon who found an arterial bleeder underneath and behind the uterus of the patient. She started to maintain blood pressure and developed a return to a normal heart rhythm after the bleeding stopped. We found out later her husband was facedown in the hospital chapel, "giving her to God" to do His will with her life. At the moment we stopped the bleeding, someone went to tell the husband she'd probably survive. The next hurdle was waiting for her to awaken, as two hours of CPR usually do not result in a good neurological outcome. She was comatose overnight in ICU, and the next morning was awake and mentally intact. A family was kept together. The next story was an even longer code blue, with longer CPR, which resulted in a miracle.

My most memorable miracle was J. C. She was in her thirties with eight children and an absent husband. Her youngest was three months old. She did not do drugs but did smoke cigarettes. She had a heart attack, an anterior wall MI (the left ventricle or powerhouse portion of the heart muscle). She went to the cardiac-catheterization lab and was brought back to our CCU stable. Her coronary arteries were clear, without plaque. As I got her settled in bed, her heart suddenly went into ventricular tachycardia, a rapid, life-threatening rhythm. Her heart basically wasn't pumping blood effectively anymore, and she had no pulse. We quickly started CPR after calling a code blue. We placed an intra-aortic balloon pump in her after we'd intubated her. They figured her "clear" coronary arteries had some vasospasm from the nicotine (which spasms the artery closed, so no blood can get through), and that caused her MI, and now the irritated heart muscle was electrically unstable. We did CPR off and on for two and a half hours. Her rhythm would briefly stabilize, but her heart wasn't pumping effectively enough to perfuse, and she'd go right back into the lethal rhythm. My fellow RN and I were praying as we helped. No one in that room wanted to stop because of her age and eight kids who wouldn't have any parent if she died. (Plus, her coronary arteries were clear.) After two and a half hours, she suddenly stayed in a normal, effectively pumping rhythm. She started to stir and followed commands, a good sign. After two and a half hours of CPR, which at its best is about 30 percent as effective as a normal rhythm and normally pumping heart, we did not know if she would be intact neurologically. By the next morning, she was extubated, awake, and talking. She heard "thousands of angels singing" just before she woke up and told me she had been in the arms of Jesus and was being rocked back and forth. Jesus told her it wasn't time yet and He loved her. It was not our skills that saved her, though the good CPR protected her brain function. The good Lord decided to leave those eight kids *with* a mom who loved them.

Thank you all who did the wonderful CPR for two and a half hours and doctors F. and B. You know who you are. God bless you forever, J. C.; I love you.

Many years later, I saw an article on the front page of our Sacramento paper with her picture on it (she still had four kids with her). They were homeless and at a local shelter. I called the newspaper, and they gave me her number. I called her and arranged for some MDs and fellow RNs to help me gift her with money, household supplies, and clothes. By this time, she was in a low-rent apartment with no furniture or household items. The last time I saw her, she was standing with her four children in a mountain of gifts. I pray for her still.

"But as for you, be strong and do not give up, for your work will be rewarded."

— 2 Chronicles 15:7

TEACHING MOMENT

You will see good and bad, but above all, learn from it. Miracles happen just as much as tragedies. You may have times when all you seem to see are tragedies, but the miracles are all around you. Be open with your eyes and heart to see them. The good does balance out the bad.

IT TAKES A TEAM

How do you define a "team"? In our neuro critical-care unit, we had a team that invested time into every patient and family who came through our doors. There might be a special MD or nurse or social worker, but it took the efforts of the entire team to affect, heal, and alter trajectories in people's lives. Our team consisted of management, day and night shift supervisors, many staff RNs, a social worker, case manager, chaplain, dietician, physical therapist, speech therapist, occupational therapist, lab techs, a pharmacist, pharmacy techs, housekeepers (now called "environmental services"), respiratory therapists, MRI, X-ray, CT, nuclear med, EKG, ultrasound, EEG, and echocardiogram techs, pain team, and last but not least, central supply and the palliative-care team. The respiratory therapists were "in the thick" of the care for the sickest patients. I tried to thank each person and get to know them as people because we all had a common goal, the patient. The sickest medical patients frequently had multiple MDs, too, to cover head, heart, lung, gut, kidney, blood dyscrasias, and infection. There was rarely, ever, one thing wrong with an ICU patient. We would round every morning with the MD, the patient's RN, and a pharmacist. We went over every single pertinent detail of their care, from psychological to emotional and physical. Later in the morning, we rounded with the dietician, speech, physical, occupational therapists, case manager, and social worker (and of course, the RN and MD again) to plan future placement and progress, i.e., rehab, home, or acute or chronic nursing care.

We had family rounds or meetings every few days with each patient's family. This is where the MD and pertinent family members met to answer all questions and give updates, progress, and future goals. Often, the family needed as much help as the patient. Many family meetings were to talk about turning off life support because there was nothing we could do to "fix" their loved one.

We also helped each other as staff. I'd had a bad headache for almost two months after bad flu and mentioned it to a neurologist I had known for many years. He slipped me into a crowded schedule right away, did an MRI, and diagnosed migraines. I'd had multiple MDs I'd known give me anesthesia, do knee surgeries, a laparoscopic cholecystectomy, two cardiac stress tests for premature ventricular contractions, an upper and lower endoscopy for anemia, and a couple of breast biopsies. I had often cared for MDs and coworkers as patients also. I learned a peer can have a major effect on your life in a moment where you "blow it." I helped a cardiologist place a temporary pacemaker wire in a patient having a big anterior wall MI that was in the third-degree block (a heart attack in a major heart-muscle area, having possible lethal arrhythmias). We stopped the patient from dying. As I cleaned the site and dressed the line-insertion area, I noticed a stopcock turned a "funny way." I turned the stopcock back to what I thought was a normal position and heard the alarms go off, showing a dropped blood pressure and slowing heart rate. The patient was back in the third-degree block and was very symptomatic, clammy, and shocky. By turning the stopcock, I'd snapped the pacer wire in half. I grabbed the cardiologist and was upset I'd caused this.

Bless his heart (thank you, Dr. M.); the cardiologist just said, "Get another pacer wire and let's slip one in right away." We pulled out the broken wire, slipped a new one into position, and the patient was fine and stable again. I was a wreck. I was distraught and crying and profusely apologizing to the MD (who was also my friend), saying, "I should quit nursing; I'm a bad nurse." He hugged me and said, "*No*, just recognize your mistake, learn from it, and never do it again." I *never* made that mistake again. I stayed in nursing for thirty more years. The MD always used to tease me when a pacer insertion would come up by saying, "Are you sure there isn't someone else who could help me with this?" He would be smiling when he said this. An RN house supervisor and a renal MD (good friend) helped admit my mom when she was very ill twice. A cardiologist in Mount Shasta gave me advice and comforted me when my husband was becoming schizophrenic.

We often sent cards and flowers to ill or grieving staff members. We had birthday parties and potlucks for each other. We even involved patients and their families at times with practical jokes or gifts. We played roles in patients' weddings and proposals. One of the important roles an ICU RN plays is to interpret what the MD just said to the family. When someone is distraught, in pain or shock over the news of a loved one's life-altering illness, they seem to hear things selectively, especially when the MD comes. I would step in and ask if they understood all that was said and what questions I could answer. Sometimes they had a good grasp of it, and sometimes they understood nothing. Other times, they'd say the MD said they could go home now, and I would say, "No, you know he didn't; you aren't well enough yet." It was shocking that the family or patient sometimes heard something completely different than you from the MD. It's because it's what they wanted to hear. When you throw culture, language, and age differences in there, it magnifies the issue. All I know is it's *never* one person who saves a patient's life. It is the concern and work of a very talented team. Communication is key here. Any time any one of us found out something new and pertinent about the patient or family, we would tell the appropriate people to increase the quality of our care.

> *"I will search for the lost and bring back the strays. I will bind up the injured and strengthen the weak."*
>
> — Ezekiel 34:16

TEACHING MOMENT

There is nothing like a cohesive trained team. Teamwork creates trust and encourages and builds up your strengths. It makes an intense situation easier to bear. Suggestions and ideas flow, and far fewer mistakes happen. Multiple minds can often see through and into the most difficult of problems while finding ways to solve things one of you cannot.

Intensive care is not for all nurses, just as emergency room or oncology or pediatrics aren't for all. It depends on your interest, heart, and God-given strengths. I was sent to work in ICU in Pinole, California, after one year from graduation only because I'd taken a heart-rhythm class. I could then identify the different arrhythmias. I have to admit I hated it at first. I saw horribly ill people who were never going to get better (like a woman who tried to kill herself by drinking Drain cleaner). The issues to fix were many and all difficult to deal with for me. I moved with my new husband to Mount Shasta because it was the first job I could find in a small town. We wanted to be out of the city. At Mount Shasta, in their four-bed ICU/CCU, I saw everything: car crashes, semitruck accidents, mountain accidents, logging accidents, snow-blower accidents, small-town traumas like stabbing, gunshot wounds, and trees falling on people and animals. I learned more in four and a half years there than many years in a big city.

"Intense" means: existing in an extreme degree, strained to the utmost, or felt deeply. Any type of nursing has times of intensity, but eight to twelve hours of it at once was very hard to deal with, at times. The knowledge level is high. You frequently need other certifications: CCRN, trauma certification, stroke RN, or neuro certification. I had my CCRN for over twenty years. CCRN is a certification for a higher overall level of critical-care nursing knowledge about every body system. To keep it current, we had to take more classes than we did just for the

RN license, teach, write papers, and/or be on committees and collaborations with multiple hospital nursing teams. We have certain requirements for learning, mandatory by hospital and state to keep certifications, job, and RN license. I, personally, never felt qualified to touch a patient with a specific problem unless I knew enough about it to have a comfort level with it. When I had a patient with a condition or disease I wasn't familiar with, I took a class or read up on it. When I didn't understand how a balloon pump worked, I took classes and studied, then jumped in and started helping with every single one I could. When we changed from CCU to neuro, only eight hours' worth of classes were given. A mandatory number of other (thirty of forty hours' worth) online classes were asked to be completed within several months. Again, I felt like a duck out of water, as my expertise was in heart and hemodynamics. I took many hundreds of hours of classes in the community over the first several years to feel competent and worthy. Changes happen daily in technology, and the amounts of lifesaving equipment we used and meds to know were overwhelming at times. Learning it was one thing; keeping up with it was another. There were many hours of mandatory skills in labs and online learning, all necessary to keep us at a high level of knowledge. I used to tell students you cannot blame someone else nor have someone else do something you're scared to do because "the buck stops here." Because of your RN license, you are the one person sometimes holding the patients' life in your hands. You can't second-guess an emergent IV drug you just pushed through a central line. You cannot always have someone right next to you, helping you make every single decision. The training and your mental fortitude have to hold you through the seconds it takes to make a life-and-death decision. The highest

Debra Bauguess

intensity shifts, where I literally ran all day and never stopped and every single minute tried to figure out what life-and-death action, med, or decision to use next were mind-numbing, when over. I spoke gibberish after using what felt like every brain cell some days. Thank God, every day was not that intense. I found the intensity a little harder to deal with upon aging, mostly the multitasking and running up and down hallways in CT and MRI marathons. My aging improved the head knowledge, competence, and confidence with most aspects of critical care. You do gain wisdom and find it easier to see the whole picture. I had cared for so many different types of ICU patients that I had personal knowledge of all the other issues the patient had, other than those our specialized unit dealt with.

"Intense" means you deal with extremes. That means emotional as well as mental and physical. The relationship between a caring ICU RN and her patient or family is intensely fast-growing due to life-and-death decisions being made in a short amount of time. In one shift, I sometimes felt a connection, bond, or closeness to someone who was very deep, who I didn't know twelve hours before. When a loved one is on the precipice and you are the lifeline for the patient and the family, they cling to what gives them hope. The phone calls are frequent and emotional. The hugs are born of desperation, and they hold onto you as if they're afraid to let go. They need you, your knowledge, caring, kindness, and love to help them just get through an overwhelming situation. It was very hard to *give* so much intensity in love to a deeply hurting family and then come home and deal with an equally intense family issue. There were times of burnout where I temporarily felt as if I had nothing else left to give and I was tapped out. That's when you recharge your batteries through faith, rest, self-care, and for me, nature. You take a break or a vacation and get your mind completely off all the pain in other people's lives. You are then able to come back refreshed and ready to give your all again.

Imagine this: a young man comes in with an acute MI (heart attack), and you find out he's a newly diagnosed diabetic. He speaks no English, has no home or address, doctor, or health insurance. The MD tells you, "Find him a doctor, get him insurance, and teach him about his two new diseases." The team goes to work, facing many, many obstructions, but they always persevere. I remember receiving an unconscious Russian-speaking patient in cardiogenic shock. Dr. M. and I placed an arterial line, pacemaker, Swan-Ganz catheter (a central IV line, placed through the heart to measure pressures in the heart), and balloon pump, then got an interpreter and whisked him off to open-heart surgery. It was 8:30 p.m., and I'd been there since 6:30 a.m. I still had all my charting to do because you cannot chart when you are physically doing procedures to save a life. I charted with bleary eyes and stumbled out to my car, sometimes to drive home and not even remember the route I took.

I would go to work with the attitude that "every day a life will touch yours, or you will touch a life." I would ask myself, "Did I make a difference in someone's life today?" I would pray before bed, "Let me rest in peace if I helped just one person." I also gave my horrors seen, regrets, or sorrow to God to handle so I could rest and sleep to go back again the next day and do it all again. Some people would try ICU and leave after some time. It was not for them. I was drawn to the intensity of the relationships formed that were cemented in love only God could provide. It did take a toll on my body, though. I have arthritis from my family history and forty-two years of lifting heavy patients. Pushing beds with patients to and from CT, MRI, and scans and rolling people back and forth twenty times a day to clean them up or pull them up or change their sheets breaks your back. Yes, we do have help, sort of; the lifts do not do what you need when you need them, and the "lift team" was not created until my last two years of work. Even then, you had to wait for them when your patient was lying in a wet bed or was halfway onto the floor, hanging off the bed. In other words: we couldn't wait and mostly did way too much by ourselves.

I wanted to mention the emotional intensity. Besides grieving, tragedy, and high stress levels of care, there was violence. It definitely increased through the years. Patients come in drunk, high, suicidal, or mentally ill. The mental illnesses frequently were acute psychotic breaks of mania or schizophrenia. The drugs were cocaine, methamphetamines, any kind of Speed, heroin, any kind of "downers" or narcotics, and sometimes PCP or LSD. These patients would be in full-blown peak-usage levels or in withdrawal or overdosed, on life support. We never knew what to expect when they woke up or "came down." It got very scary. We would call code gray to get security, extra hands, and supervisors whenever we felt threatened. Many patients were elderly and having dementia or Alzheimer's moments. Many were distraught family members upset at the condition of their loved one in the bed (even though we had nothing to do with them being there). Local gang members would try to come in and "finish" off someone who had survived their first attempt to kill him. I've had many patients lunge at me and dodged punches and kicks and scathing curse words. We even had to take several types of self-defense classes each year and classes in recognition of escalating issues. These violent episodes happened more frequently in certain units: ER, ICU (especially trauma and neuro because of brain damage), and any psych ward.

I have been very scared several times but can say I made it through forty-two years of intensity in every form of the word and survived it and loved it, overall. It did make adjusting to retirement harder because you are used to intensity, and let's say it, retirement just isn't that intense. It's actually peaceful, restful, and well earned. I'm adjusting now, but the first year does take time to figure out where you fit in. I did projects around the house that had been put off and am now writing this book to keep myself busy. The need to help people is still there, and I'm working out how to do that through my church compassion team.

> *"He gives strength to the weary and increases the power of the weak."*
>
> — Isaiah 40:29

TEACHING MOMENT

There are degrees of intensity. Get into whatever level you are happiest with. Ask others and learn how to deal with intense situations. Take the appropriate classes to learn the lifesaving techniques until you are comfortable with them.

THE SACRIFICE

In any job, you sacrifice. In most jobs, you sacrifice sleep or time with kids and family. In twenty-four-hour-a-day nursing, you do shift work and sacrifice normal work hours. I worked a little of nights, a lot of evening shifts (three p.m. to midnight, my favorite), and the last twenty-five or so years on days (twelve-hour shifts). I worked many "doubles" (sixteen-hour shifts) and much overtime over the years. I worked an eighteen-hour shift once and did four to five twelve-hour shifts in a row several times. You get up, work, come home, go to bed, and get up again. Until retirement, I didn't know what it was like to have all the holidays or every weekend off. As a nurse, you give up family time on Thanksgiving and Christmas. We always had our holidays several days before or after. I worked Christmas a lot because of the families with kids. I always told myself, "The patients don't want to be there on the holiday either." You miss church two or three times a month and sometimes never feel like a part of anything due to irregular, long hours and days worked. You sacrifice your joints, mostly knees, back, shoulders, and neck. Neuro ICU has many comatose patients, and you lift, lift, lift, and lift some more. You crawl under heavy machinery and equipment, turn, pull, push, and drag heavy beds with the patient in them to CT, MRI, nuclear med, and other procedures—daily (usually on the other side of the large hospital). The beds with patients in them can weigh up to 1,000 pounds. No wonder my back hurts.

You miss, whether accidentally or self-chosen, breaks, lunch, water, coffee, sitting down, and bathroom breaks—to save the patient. You cannot leave a room to go to the bathroom when you are covered in a sterile gown and are in the middle of a lifesaving procedure. We did help each other get ten minutes of respite when we could. Many days we got all our breaks, but many we did not. You sacrifice hurt, pain, and sorrow in yourself to bear another's so you can lessen their load. You sacrifice your health, in general (so do schoolteachers), as you are around disease, bacteria, and viruses all day long. You sacrifice nice nails and smooth skin on your hands due to gloves being on and off hundreds of times a day, as well as hand washing and alcohol foam to the point of cracked, bleeding fingertips. Health department rules would have us wash three times as much as we did, and many nurses had raw, hurting hands with rashes and cuts, as it was.

You now see and smell many things you never wanted to. Stool, urine, vomit, infection, and blood all have unique smells. If you cannot deal with anything beyond a baby's diapers, maybe caregiving is not for you. Just put yourself in their place and realize that you, too, may need cleaning up someday. Many families care for their elderly dementia parents at home and have to deal with messes. It's a fact of life, and "what goes in must come out." Obviously, if you cannot stand the sight of blood, do not become a lab tech, do not become a paramedic or EMT, and do not work in ER or ICU or OB. In ICU, you give up your right not to have to deal with anything obnoxious, whether sights, smells, or upset patients. It is a choice, and it is extreme at times. I would advise you to ask someone in the profession you chose about it before you go into it. You do not want to end up in a job doing something you absolutely cannot stomach or make yourself do. You can choose any number of different nursing paths, however. You could work in rehab, clinic, teaching in nursing schools, etc. There are nursing jobs that do not deal with smells or sights beyond your sensibilities. You ultimately sacrifice a life of bliss and ignorance to see, hear, and feel all of life's heartache, pain, and tragedy. Sacrifice is giving of yourself for the sake of your fellow human being to receive something real, deep and life-sustaining. It *is* worth it.

> *"Follow God's example, therefore, as dearly loved children and walk in the way of love, just as Christ loved us and gave himself up for us as a fragrant offering and sacrifice to God."*

— Ephesians 5:1–2

TEACHING MOMENT

The sacrifice is worth it if you love your job, love people, and love yourself. Any job has sacrifice. Nursing has many more than some, with twenty-four-hour care and shift work and the foibles of individual personalities of hurting patients and families. Be very sure this is a direction you want to go in. There is no greater reward than to help your fellow human being.

WHAT NOT TO DO. WHEN TO ASK FOR HELP. WHEN TO BEND THE RULES

There are many, many "never dos." There are critical IV drugs you cannot give too fast or too slow. There are IV meds that don't mix or "play well" with each other in the same IV line (needing a second or third or fourth IV site or line). There are procedures with "to do" and "not to do" guidelines and risks. The head of the bed being up or down can kill a patient. If they have high brain pressure or sick lungs, head down makes them worse. If they have low blood pressure or a failing, shocky heart, head up makes them worse. Positioning on one side or the other (especially with a sick lung) can rapidly worsen the patient. Visitors who agitate or overstimulate can harm the patient. A brain recovering from an injury cannot handle too much stimulation at times; it's absorbed with healing itself. Feeding can hurt a patient in certain circumstances, and families always want us to feed their loved ones. If they've had a stroke that paralyzes half the swallowing muscles, they cannot handle water, ice, or any liquid or solid: they choke because whatever you place in their mouth goes straight into their lungs. If they are too sleepy, they cannot swallow. Temperature (too hot or too cold) can be therapy or harm, and families always come into the room and put an extra blanket on the bed over the patient. We have to explain that we are fighting a fever (from brain injury or infection) or deliberately cooling them for brain protection. It's hard not to throw a blanket on when your loved one is shivering. We "cool" people down after CPR to give the brain a chance to recover. We "cool" people down with any temperature over 36.5 centigrade with special cooling blankets, IV lines, and machines to keep the metabolism down to help a "swollen" brain. About the only time we "warm" people is after they are found in cold conditions (water, snow, home on the floor for days after collapsing, etc.) We do have several meds and air warming blankets for topical warming we give to help the shivering.

You never want to feel infallible or self-righteous because things happen when you least expect it, good and bad. You can never know enough or stop asking questions or stop double and triple-checking everything you give. The students who didn't ask for help scared me. Once you've been an RN for twenty or more years, you may only need to ask for help when you really need it, i.e., something happening out of your control. I would rather ask for a double-check on a med or procedure, even as an experienced RN, than harm a patient. I don't care if they think I'm forgetful or incompetent. Double-checking shows that you are human; you realize mistakes can happen to the best of us, and you care. Double-checking, especially when you're tired or not feeling well, hungry (low sugar levels), or dehydrated, is worth any comment by another as long as your patient gets the correct, safe care. I learned to ask for help when I needed more than two hands. Usually, it was help turning, cleaning up, or lifting. Sometimes it was an imminent code blue (patient about to die) or violence about to happen. We *all* ran to any room when another RN or MD or caregiver yelled, "Help!" I learned it's better to ask for help and help others when they ask so as *not* to get physically hurt, trying to do it alone. The invincible young nurses would say, "You can do it yourself; I do." They don't realize they will be "me" in forty years, with low back, neck, and spine degeneration from arthritis and lifting (too many times by myself). Do not apologize for asking for help when you truly need it. On the other hand, make an attempt to always help others unless it pulls you away from something literally life-and-death. Other nurses see it as "what goes around comes around." It only takes a few minutes to help and much longer to live down "unit talk" about you not helping when others ask.

About words and talking: watch what you say and how you say it and your tone of voice to everyone, peers and patients. Never discuss a patient's private life unless it's within the context of a healing-care team's need to know. *Never be rude*, condescending, or unkind to *anyone*. There is *no excuse*. Take a deep breath and walk away if angry or upset.

Laughing at the nursing station, six feet from a dying patient's room, is always inappropriate. Loud talking or conversations or laughter need to be in closed rooms at night when patients are sleeping or when patients need quiet to heal. Gossip among peers or about patients hurts *all* involved. You get back what you give and may find yourself the recipient of what you dish out. You can be tactful, authoritative, and blunt if dealing with someone unruly but never harsh, angry, or punitive. I'm definitely not perfect and never will be and have had my share of all of these mistakes but see now how we should strive daily to be. Hindsight is always so much easier.

Rules have reasons for being made, at some level, but need to be bent for the welfare of the patient sometimes. I would give food with salt (soup) to a dying patient, even though they had high blood pressure. I would give coffee (caffeine) to a cardiac patient with two months to live or extra ice to a desperately thirsty patient that was NPO (nothing by mouth) if their stomach tube would suck out all the water. There is nothing worse than a dry, parched mouth. We saw that over and over again as one of the patients' main complaints. I *never* bent a rule without a good cause and almost always had a supervisor agree to it. In Pinole, I had a husband sneak a small dog in a large bag into his wife's room for twenty minutes the night before her major surgery. It calmed her fears, and she rested well that night. The dog was clean, had its shots, was quiet, and gave unconditional love and hope to a woman scared of dying. I let a dog in to lie on her mother's lap after we'd extubated her and taken her life support off. She lived alone with this companion, and it was her only wish as she died. She comfortably stopped breathing, holding her furry baby. We rolled patients on special gurney chairs or in their beds outside to feel air and sunshine after prolonged time in the ICU.

Mostly, I let visitors in who would positively affect the patient and/or sustain the person visiting with hope and gratefulness. At the end of a shift, my newly admitted patient was crying. Half her body did not move from a recent stroke. Her church choir (about six ladies) was in the waiting room and politely asked if they could quietly sing a worship song to their friend in bed, then they'd leave. The *rules* said, "No more than two at a time for five minutes and never at a shift change." My student and I talked and let them in, briefly, for the sake of all concerned. We closed the doors, and as they sang a beautiful song to their friend, the patient smiled crookedly and raised her affected paralyzed hand up to worship with them. *All* were filled with hope and amazement at a miracle. The student and

I were crying and hugging as other RNs gave us the look for breaking the rules. I will *always* put my patient first. Once, I had a brain-dead patient, and we finally found the family to come in and hear about the wonderful possibility of organ donation. It gives meaning to the loss of the loved one, as others live on through their dying gift. The two family members finally agreed, with much sorrow, to do it and asked if they could say goodbye to their loved one. They were tired and had driven quite a ways to be there at our request. Again, it's the change of shift, but I let them into the room to say their goodbyes and also to thank them for their love in "giving" their loved one to others to help them live. I shut the doors so they would hear no other shift talk about other patients. A fellow RN came by, opened the doors, and rudely told them they could not be there and had to leave immediately. I went in and apologized and explained about HIPAA (patient privacy) but told them they were welcome to stay as long as they needed, but I would shut the doors. Again, the family and I had that shared knowledge of grace and mercy given in a time of need. If someone was dying, I would always let some family in at the change of shift and just explain about privacy and shut the doors. If any single one of the nurses who stuck to the rules had ever spent time with their own dying loved one in a hospital at the shift change, they would change their ways. Mercy and grace and kindness (while keeping the patient's privacy in the report) go a lot further in a world full of anger and fear than sticking to rules. I was on an interunit committee run by the director of critical-care nursing at one time, where we found that the nationwide findings were that visiting should be open. There were other ways for every nurse to control the situation per patient and family member every shift. ICU RNs are very controlling, which is needed most of the time for patient safety, but the control got to be for their lives to be made easier, not the patient's. All I can say is, "Put yourself in their shoes." If it were your husband, wife, child, mom, or dad dying, you would feel you had the right to be there (especially when the loved one is not conscious). Admittedly, there were always problem visitors and families with who everyone had trouble, but more often than not, they were hurting, lost, grieving loved ones grateful for every single kind word or deed. Three days before my retirement, my Christian supervisor allowed the daughter and husband in to see their dying mom. With Covid rules, no one came in! She let me have them come in, knowing they were healthy, had no fever, and had masks and gloves on, and *it was the right thing to do*. When it's the right thing to do in God's eyes, I will fight to bend the rules every time. The undying gratitude I have for my charge RN who allowed this is eclipsed by the lifelong gratitude that daughter and husband have for the time spent seeing a loved one "in the flesh" for the last time. I would have moved heaven and earth to be with my mom if she was dying. When someone knows you did everything in your power to help them because you care, it's priceless to *both* sides. I'm sounding very self-righteous, I'm sure, to you, but I've learned these hard lessons from forty-two years in ICU. I know that I know what is the right thing to do *now*. I may not have, many times in the past, but I do now.

I now find myself in the same situation I just described: my mom is extremely ill with pneumonia and heart failure in a hospital (non-COVID-19). The rules are "No more than one person visiting the entire length of stay even if he or she's dying." There is only my brother and me. We have both been unable to get the required COVID-19 test results they want in the time frame the hospital specifies. My mom is scared, weak, and alone, without a single visitor. This is morally and ethically wrong on every level.

I feel the rules reflecting the fear of COVID-19 are tearing our nation asunder right now. Family is at the heart of God's love. To deny a proven-healthy family a chance to see a possibly dying loved one breaks your heart in two. I've been dealing with anger, hurt, disappointment, and grief over a country gone mad. After forty-two years of "doing the right thing" and having compassion and empathy for others, can I not expect myself to be treated the same? I'm praying for the strength to let go of any untoward feelings and let God's will ensue. I pray for comfort beyond myself for all involved. I am truly shocked at how the opposite of what I'm writing about is enforced in our world today. Lord, help us understand and let Your will, purpose, and plan unfold.

I'm not advocating going out and breaking every rule a hospital makes; they are for a reason and good, most of the time. Some rules can be bent if it changes a human being's life and attitude toward the place of care and the caregiver and benefits the patient. Isn't nursing about *healing*? Obviously, there are absolute rules with medicines and practice; I did *not* bend those. Dealing with human beings when they are hurting, look for a *safe* way to help them by "bending" a rule if it shows mercy and gives grace and leaves an everlasting thankfulness in their hearts.

I need to send out a special thank-you to a woman named Patty. She is everything I've talked about in this book. She went out of her way to assist me in finding out my COVID-19 test result. The hospital where my mom was deathly ill only had a seventy-two-hour window from test to result, when you could visit in. Patty called me multiple times at home, reassuring me that she was calling the lab in Arizona and trying all things possible to get my results in time. They never came, but she stayed overtime by forty minutes at work and gave me one last phone call, saying she was still trying. You see, she could not catch a flight in time to see her dying mom; she understood my desperation. Only those who have been in your shoes and are compassionate, empathetic human beings will go the extra mile for a stranger. May God bless you and your family forever, dear Patty. You give me faith in the caregivers out there who "give" from their hearts to sow love.

> *"Discretion will protect you, and understanding will guard you."*
>
> — Proverbs 2:11

> *"Do not withhold good from those to whom it is due, when it is in your power to act."*
>
> — Proverbs 3:27

> *"The words of the reckless pierce like a sword, but the tongue of the wise brings healing."*
>
> — Proverbs 12:18

> *"A gentle answer turns away wrath, but a harsh word stirs up anger."*
>
> — Proverbs 15:1

Debra Bauguess

"The tongue has the power of life and death, and those who love it will eat its fruit."

— Proverbs 18:21

TEACHING MOMENT

Do not go and just break the rules. You will see times where small, important "bending" of the rules changes a person's life for the better. Never place anyone in a compromising moment or place of danger with your "bending" of the rule. Run it by your supervisor and safely do what your heart tells you will benefit the patient.

WHEN IT HAPPENS
TO YOU

I learned "bad things happen to good people," and I learned how to help strangers through trials. When it's someone you know or your family, it changes your perspective, usually for the better, because you now know how your patients feel. I took care of many hospital acquaintances and friends. I took care of three long-time known MDs with heart attacks. I took care of celebrity families. I gave money to World Vision and sponsored a child for many years in Ghana, Africa. I had a patient with the same name from Ghana, probably the same village. It's such a small world. My quiet neighbor, who I rarely saw outside, became known to me because I took care of his father as he died in our ICU. Now, we talk.

At my drive-through coffee place (06:10 every work a.m.), there's a young woman whose grandmother I cared for. An anesthesiologist I'd always thought was gruff and unapproachable became a friend after I took care of his dad in the ICU. His dad was a character; I grew to love him and know the anesthesiologist saw me differently after seeing me truly care about his dad. There was a young man with the most beautiful tenor voice I've ever heard who sang at my large church. I took care of his father, and upon my break, on my birthday, my co-workers had the son (whose voice I loved) come into the break room and sing "Happy Birthday" to me. Wow!

Recently, we added a new RN to our neuro ICU, and her face and name seemed so familiar. She said I'd taken care of her when she was very ill, in my CCU twenty years before. We are sisters at heart today, as she loves Jesus as I do. My best friend and RN in Mount Shasta was my patient in recovery in my ICU for an emergent ruptured ovarian cyst. She almost died. I helped save the life of an X-ray tech at Mercy San Juan, who was in ventricular tachycardia; I had to shock his heart. His wife and I saw each other recently as he was recovering in our neuro unit, almost twenty years later. Many hospital friends were in our ICU post-op. A dear friend with a venous thrombus (blood clot in a brain vein) was my patient. It's always a pleasure to care for someone you deeply care about. My best friend went into the hospital with severe belly pain. The first time, it was dead bowel needing surgery. Now, the second time, her other friend came to me at work and begged me to help her. She was up on another floor in pain, waiting for an X-ray of her belly to be read. I spoke to her MD, explained our relationship and my experience, and said, "Please do not sit on this, call a surgeon; it was dead bowel last time." He listened, and she was in OR within one hour, and it probably saved her life. My dear RN friend's husband died of cancer, and we went through much of it with her. She sobbed on my shoulder once while I held her. I never did get the lipstick out of that dress, but I consider it well worth it. I had two knee surgeries and a lap chole (a procedure to remove the gallbladder). Two of the three times, my anesthesia didn't agree with me, and I did not have fun. The first knee surgery was great, and I would choose that anesthetist any day.

It helps to know your MDs. My husband was very ill with a cat bite, which sent infection into his thumb joint. A great ortho MD at Mount Shasta fixed him. I would work and go on my breaks to admit him, start his IV, and push some of his antibiotics. My dad was in my neuro ICU with a possible stroke, and my neurointensivist friend asked if there was anything he shouldn't bring up with my dad when he went in to check on him. I told him about three touchy subjects that always set my dad off. He said, "Okay," and went into the room, sat down, and got relaxed, asking my dad about how he felt about all three of those touchy subjects. Of course, my dad went on a rant and gave his doc an earful. The MD said he "was just doing a good neuro exam." When my aunt was getting blood transfusions weekly in Vancouver, Washington, I had flown up to be with her. I sat with her for about eight hours one day (she got two units of blood) and got to know the nurses and other patients around her quite well. The RNs taking care of her were delightful and actually wanted me to come work there. It really would have been a great job. My mom had multiple serious surgeries over about fifteen years, and I spent many hours at her bedside pre and post-op, just reading or sometimes dealing with questions she or the RNs and MDs had. My experience really helped then. I made her go to the hospital once because I knew she was really ill, and though she didn't want to, she did. It turned out she was septic from bacteria in her spine. Her MD, Dr. A., had me call him at home at 10:30 p.m. on his vacation to answer my questions. To this day, I've never met anyone like him. He's one of my hero MDs. When I was hit once by my husband, I went to work with a bruised mouth and lied to my friend, an ER RN, about how it happened. I was so ashamed. She told me later she knew I'd been hit and was lying. Nurses get very good at reading people and many times get a sixth sense about other things going on in people's lives.

I struggled physically at work in an intense lifting environment due to my arthritis. The arthritis was partly hereditary and a lot—injury from years of lifting. I don't recommend for-ty-one years of ICU to students because of that alone (it's so very physical), but I do not regret one single minute of it.

I learned, when my dad died in memory care, that to not be with someone you love when they die is horrible. I'm still personally dealing with regret that I didn't stay with him as he got sicker. (I lived an hour away and was working full-time.) Be gentle with yourself when grieving; it makes you fragile. It does, however, help you better understand those who grieve. During COVID-19, I firmly believe a mistake was made in not allowing immediate family in as their loved ones suffered and sometimes died, specifically when they were afebrile and healthy and wore appropriate protective gear and stayed briefly. Obviously, there was the issue of enough protective gear for our own nurses, but a one-time brief visit to see a loved one's face before they died would have changed so very many lives for the better. There is no substitute, ever, for a loved one being at your bedside as you die. The nurses told the families they would love on them like their own and did, *but* the broken hearts on both sides when death separates you and you are not together at that last moment cannot be repaired. So many died alone, even though the nurses did their very best with the constraints of COVID-19.

Praise be to God and Father of our Lord Jesus Christ,
the Father of compassion and the God of all comfort,
who comforts us in all our troubles, so that we can
comfort those in any trouble with the comfort we our-
selves receive from God.

— 2 Corinthians 1:3–4

Debra Bauguess

TEACHING MOMENT

We all have our home life and work life. Try to keep them separate. A lot of overlap isn't always helpful. Seek help for yourself and/or take time off if outside issues make it difficult to be there for your patients. Most employers allow stress leave or personal time off to deal with the crisis at home. You need to be on your A game in ICU, so help yourself first and try to come to work always with the right attitude and strength to do your best for these very sick patients.

NEVER STOP LEARNING, TEACHING

I learned fast, as a newly christened RN with a bachelor's degree, in my first couple of weeks on a fifty-bed surgical floor, that there's nothing too lowly to help others with. When the aides, orderlies, and LVNs see a BSN help them answer lights and clean up messes shoulder to shoulder, they will help you when you need it. They put me in charge within my first few weeks of work. I was scared to death but "dug in" and asked for help and advice a lot.

Never stop asking questions. One thing I learned about nursing is that the more you learn, the more you learn you don't know. Every patient is unique, and no human body responds the same to meds or procedures. Your skill, your knowledge, and your will to help are challenged every minute of every day. Almost nothing goes exactly as planned, and *anything* can happen at *any* time. The most stable patient can crash, and the most critical can improve overnight. I learned that I have no right to touch a patient with a specific set of symptoms or do a procedure I knew nothing about. Their life is literally in my hands. I admitted to MDs my not knowing how to do something and said I'd be willing to learn and help. If a new piece of equipment or procedure scared me, I took classes and learned it *well*. I usually ended up teaching it. I found a deep love for EKG reading after a Mount Shasta RN first showed me an inferior MI. She kept saying, "Just look at groupings: leads two, three, and aVF: it's an inferior MI." That sent me on a love for cardiac nursing and EKGs that eventually led me to teaching EKG classes to staff, writing an EKG module, and becoming a fifteen-year CCU unit supervisor. I also taught Advanced Cardiac Life Support for fifteen-plus years.

When balloon pumps seemed complex, I studied and ended up way out of my comfort zone, teaching per diem for Arrow International on the West Coast. I freaked out speaking in front of groups; my voice came out high and fast, and I forgot things. Once I felt the comfort and passion of knowing about the subject, I improved. I became the balloon-pump teacher at Skills Day and certifier for all the CCU, catheterization lab, and cardiac surgery RNs at Mercy San Juan for a number of years. I absolutely loved it. Cardiologists would even (when it was still new to staff) call me to come help in emergencies in the cardiac-catheterization lab and other units when it involved a balloon pump. I won a Daisy Award because of my balloon-pump knowledge. I have a vast knowledge about EKGs and have a huge book of tracings (without names) I've saved for over forty years. One cardiac surgeon used to borrow it to teach paramedics. The countless hours of neuro classes I took upon myself led to an eventual confidence level I'll always cherish in a world of new and different needs than the ones I'd known for thirty years in cardiac care ICU. I once read, "Just for today, I will try to strengthen my mind. I will study, I will learn something useful. I will not be a mental loafer. I will read something that requires effort, thought, and concentration."[1] I also learned that to concentrate, you must have adequate sleep, hydration, and a normal blood sugar level.

Learning and teaching go hand in hand. There's an old adage, "See one, do one, teach one." Once you teach a subject, you never forget it. Having a life experience teaches you how

Debra Bauguess

to teach someone else in the same situation. My prayers (in the car each morning) to be "used by God" used to play out in the course of my day frequently. One morning, reporting in, I was assigned a little older man with newly diagnosed dementia and a family new to the diagnosis. I'd spent the previous day with my dad in his dementia, and I remember inwardly telling God, "I don't want this patient; I dealt with it all day yesterday." I started off feeling put-upon and a little grumpy. It was always a challenge not to let your tiredness or irritation show to the "before" and "after" RNs in the report or the patients. After about one hour, I was half in love with the very sweet patient. He reminded me of my dad and the new gentleness and sweetness he had as he needed us more through his illness. When the patient's daughter came in, she looked scared and unsure of how to speak to her father. I had her come outside the room and sit next to me, always at eye level. I asked her what she knew about her dad's diagnosis and how she felt about it. Forty-five minutes later, I realized I'd shared most of the knowledge I'd gained the hard way with my dad's fall into dementia. I'd been able to tell her how to talk with him, what to expect next, how to help him, and how to deal with her and her mom's feelings in this frightening situation. She started crying and asked if she could hug me. She said, "No one's ever asked how I'm feeling before." I realized, as she walked away, feeling encouraged and cared for, that God "used" me. He knew exactly what assignment to give me that I was uniquely qualified for *and* knew that daughter needed me and what I had to teach that day, at that moment in time.

Another God-appointed assignment was with a sweet older woman whose husband was altered by a big stroke and would never go home again (most likely to a skilled nursing placement). I spent an hour sitting next to her, with pen and paper, prioritizing what she needed to find out at home. She would need to find bank accounts, paperwork, checkbook, trash days, legal help, etc. She was so grateful for my teaching that I'd learned the hard way with my parents. My dad's dementia and mom's concurrent severe illness left me to get a power of attorney, sell the house (reverse mortgage) with forty years of belongings, sell the car (without registration or title—lost), deal with where all the bill payers were located and what was due and when, and still deal with two ill parents. My desperate need for knowledge and help came with some scattered wonderful help, but my life was upside down for some time. My faith was tested and grew as God showed up time and again. This little old wife needing the same information showed me, once again, I'd been placed in the right place at the right time with the right person needing my unique set of hard-learned information for the day.

The MDs used to be terse or say they were too busy to answer my questions in the report (and they *were* usually overwhelmed with work). Once they understood that I truly wanted to know and learn and was interested, they would teach me. Toward the end, frequently, they would show me something new or interesting in a scan or tell me about a new concept because they knew I cared and wanted to know. They would even "quiz" me. I told my students to always ask questions and double-check and *never* stop learning. I often would let the student "fail" at something simple and unharmful or costly to learn that what I was saying was true. I found that much learning in nursing was through trial and error. It would be simple but sometimes messy things like spraying yourself with red liquid Tylenol or orange potassium liquid because you didn't secure a feed-tube connection. My prayer always was that I would never make a mistake that would harm anyone, including myself. I've jabbed myself with needles many times, though experience leads to far fewer sticks. I thank God none of them resulted in me getting a disease.

Teaching made you aware of how much you really know. Often, after spending a day with a young student, I went home feeling as if I do know things and am a worthy ICU RN. I loved presenting new situations or posing a set of symptoms to a student and watching them reason out an answer. I told stories, gave examples, showed them my books and notes, and made lists of what I wanted them to learn. I really tried to impress on them that the *most important thing was the human being in the bed.* We were given the privilege to handle a patient and their family's needs, wants, and hopes in a few hours, hopefully leaving them with the feeling of being cared about. One of my dearest students made up a top-ten list on a thank-you card for me that I expanded on and used many times with other students. She had "gotten" what I needed her to see about the art of nursing. The patient is human and worthy of love. Her first nine items covered knowing the patient, and number ten was technical: "Never push IV Dilantin faster than fifty mg. per minute." Knowing my hard work might pay off and hopefully help the future outlook of a fellow nurse in her quest to find the heart of nursing was priceless.

A young RN took care of me with my first knee surgery, and I was taken by his quiet strength, manner, and deep love for God. I came back weeks later and gave him a baby gift for his third child. He was interested in ICU, and I later helped get him into our ICU and mentored him for three months. I will always treasure those days. Even though teaching took three times the normal amount of work, it was a chosen, loved hardship. You still had your normal amount of work to get done, plus extra paperwork for the student (done at home), plus extra time given on shift as you waited long minutes for the student to perform a task, and explained everything you did and how to chart it. It was more stressful in the amount of work needed but a lifelong reward in giving back to the next generation of caregivers. I never acted as if I knew it all. I stayed humble and would say, "I don't know; I'll look it up." I would research it at work if time allowed or research it at night before our next meeting. I had mentors and fellow RNs who also taught, who are on my most-admired list. Bunkie, Don, Bev, Margaret, Bobbi, Anne, Cindy, Dan, Chris, and Judy, you know who you are. Thank you from the bottom of my heart to *all* the MDs I bugged with endless questions. You made me who I am today.

One of the most important things I ever learned was about simple reality. I used to call the cardiologist on call with multiple issues, all worsening in a patient, and as I listed numbers, lab results and tried to impress him with the patient's decline, he would stop me. He would say, "Kid, slow down. What does the patient look like, right now?" I would say, "Pink, warm, and dry and talking to me." He'd say, "Good, now what is the worst thing happening right at this moment?" He and I would then both know there were a couple of things I could do right then, and the MD had time not to rush over. I'll ever be grateful to Dr. M. for that life lesson, and you can be sure I passed it on to the students.

One of the things I will miss most is learning, teaching, and having a confidence level worthy of my calling. I am continuing to seek, learn, grow, and teach in new subjects, like my love for God and the Bible. I will never stop learning, asking,

Debra Bauguess

and gaining knowledge about a myriad of things now, in retirement.

I need to add something about critical thinking. Critical thinking cannot be taught. It's based on the need to know *now* and how to prioritize in a critical situation. It is part education, part learned skills, part mistake learned, and part intuition, all based on your collective knowledge brought forth in an instant to prevent a looming crisis. I used to see my job as a detective's role. I would spend twelve hours seeking every detail known and unknown in a patient's life story and current condition to find reasons for their illness and ways to attempt a remedy. The RN and MD work as a team. The MD is in the patient's room, sometimes for ten minutes (many times, longer), and the RN lays hands on them for twelve hours straight. You see and hear every symptom they exhibit. It worked both ways: the MD would point out something in the patient's history or neuro exam that I would learn, or I would hear a detail of past history or see a new symptom the MD didn't know about. Trying to gather a multitude of facts in an organized manner to guide a complete diagnosis is a challenge. So many little details determine a patient's outcome. Having a brain that seeks answers and always sees the challenge of delving deeper to find all you can is a gift. Knowing when to call the MD and how to present your findings or questions directs the best forward care of your patient. One or two things may be getting worse in your patient's condition, but looking for what else may get worse next and pulling together all pertinent details must be done quickly. "Critical" means a turning point, an abrupt change for better or worse, approaching a state of crisis or life and death. Waiting five minutes to act or call can affect someone's outcome for the worse. You have to rely on facts, past experience (you've seen that before), and intuition (gut feeling) to guide you in emergent treatments. You cannot teach someone to prioritize. They must have a deep knowledge of the basics. Knowing the ABCs is critical.

The more complex a patient, the more you go back to basics. If they need an airway, cover every detail of fixing that. If they need help breathing, assist that. If they need sustainable blood pressure and circulation, support that. They need all three to provide life-sustaining oxygen to the brain, heart, and all other internal organs. It needs to be about basics because everything happens at a cellular level. The more advanced critical-care classes got into depth on basic life sustainment at a cell level and quickly got extremely complex. It always amazed me how utterly complex and yet marvelous the human body is. It is a dynamic, constantly changing wonder of creation. I honestly learned something new *every* day. Life can deteriorate to death in a single heartbeat. You, as the primary caregiver, must (you do not have a choice) decide, within seconds, on a direction to go and what action to take *first* while calling for help as you run. I can say, after forty-two years, I felt at the top of my game. I may not have moved as fast or multitasked as well as when I was twenty years old, but I *have* the past experience! I have "been there, done that" many times before. I knew exactly what to do in *any* emergency. I once recovered a post-cath lab patient and was carefully watching the puncture site in the groin and noticed a pulsing at the site. I listened over it with my stethoscope and heard a bruit (rhythmic "whooshing" sound). I figured the patient had a false aneurysm in their femoral artery. I was having a hard time stopping the oozing of blood. I called the MD, and he listened to me, trusted me, and ordered an ultrasound and the radiology team in to fix the new false aneurysm.

One day, my female patient would not arouse; she was stable but with low blood pressure and oxygen levels. She was too sleepy to open her eyes. We checked everything: blood sugar, lab work, arterial-blood gases, neurological exam, etc. Nothing showed us a reason. I got a gut feeling it was her heart and did a little calculation on some lab and told the head cardiologist, Dr. S., "I think her cardiac output is too low." He agreed with me, knowing my years of cardiac experience, and we placed a Swan-Ganz catheter. Her cardiac output was around three with a cardiac index of about 1.5, which is "shock" and means the heart is not pumping well and the patient needs immediate treatment. She next got a balloon pump placed and woke up. Thank you, doctors, who trust your gut instincts.

Another night, after a cardiac cath and percutaneous cardiac angioplasty (a balloon is blown up inside an artery to push the plaque apart and regain blood flow), my patient shortly developed shortness of breath, changing vital signs (lowered blood pressure and an erratic heart rate) and was having chest pain. I felt the angioplasty site was closing and the patient was in imminent danger. The MD listened and took the patient back to the cath lab and fixed the closing angioplasty site.

Many times with MDs who had worked with me for many years, I would call and say, "You need to get here immediately; the patient's going to 'code' [acutely decompensate or try to die]." I often told an MD, "The patient may need intubation or a balloon pump or a certain procedure soon; I'll keep you informed." Invariably, they did, and at least the MD was aware and ready. Good ICU RNs who know their craft and warn MDs about possible upcoming dangers are worth their weight in gold. The MDs knew they could trust us to have their back and inform them right away if the least little thing changed that could result in a catastrophe. The trust and respect you build between a critical-care MD and RN are precious and necessary and take time to build. I went from working with cardiologists and pulmonologists (lung MDs) for thirty years to new and different MDs who did not know me. By the time I left my neuro ICU (about fourteen years), I felt competent and worthy and like I'd earned respect from each of the three neurointensivists I worked with.

It takes stepping out with courage and knowledge to gather the resources needed to help in the healing of someone critically ill when a crisis appears. Take a deep breath, go back to basics, prioritize, believe in yourself (your head knowledge, training, and experience), and save that life. I never, ever took for granted the times my experience helped me lay hands on the dying and bring them back from the brink. If you lose that sense of responsibility of having someone's life in your hands as a God-given privilege, you probably shouldn't stay in ICU, or maybe even in nursing. Nursing is a job of the heart; not all RN roles deal with life and death, but things can happen in a split second to any one of us. I pray an experienced RN who can think quickly on her/his feet and use that learned knowledge will care about and for me when I'm ill.

"The fear of the LORD is the beginning of knowledge, but fools despise wisdom and instruction."

— Proverbs 1:7

Debra Bauguess

"Apply your heart to instruction and your ears to words of knowledge."

— Proverbs 23:12

Turning your ear to wisdom and applying your heart to understanding—indeed, if you call our for insight and cry aloud for understanding, and if you look for it as for silver and search for it as for hidden treasure, then you will understand the fear of the LORD *and find the knowledge of God. For the* LORD *gives wisdom; from his mouth come knowledge and understanding.*

— Proverbs 2:2–6

TEACHING MOMENT

Not everyone is a teacher, but we are all students. The only way you grow is by asking questions and looking up stuff on your own. Never stop learning. Things keep changing so fast. Don't be satisfied with reading X-ray or CT or MRI reports: look up the images and see what those changes look like. Look for moments to teach younger nurses. There is always someone more experienced than you to draw from and someone less experienced than you to coach.

THE MOST IMPORTANT THINGS TO LEARN ABOUT NURSING (ADAPTED FROM CARISSA'S ORIGINAL TOP-TEN LIST)

1. Treat the patient and family as you want to be treated.

2. With every patient and/or family visitor, every shift, make a pact to find out at least one new thing about their life that you connect with and tell them something about you. Share lives with each other. They will be on their call light less and work with you more and trust you more because they know you care about them.

3. Do not be afraid to sit and just listen.

4. Do not be afraid to *hug* and touch.

5. Do not be afraid to sit and talk about the hard things: death, code status, poor prognosis, etc. It's okay for you or the patient/family to cry.

6. Have great compassion and empathy, but never say, "I know how you feel," unless you actually have been in their exact shoes before.

7. *Never* be rude or impatient; there's never an excuse.

8. Be genuine, gentle, truthful, and honest—*always*.

9. You are dealing with people at the worst moment of their lives: acknowledge that and help them in any way you can, no matter how seemingly unimportant or little.

10. Take care of yourself; you must eat and sleep enough to think fast and clearly at all times. Conditions change too fast in ICU.

11. Never assume you won't make a mistake; you will. Triple-check any med (especially IV) that you give in ICU.

12. Always keep learning and asking questions.

13. If a patient starts to worsen acutely, check on what drips are hanging and what IV or PO med they just had. What can you shut off or correct with an antidote?

14. Never push IV Dilantin faster than fifty mg. per minute.

THE ONLY CONSTANT
IS CHANGE.
THEN AND NOW

Change is very difficult for most, as it takes you out of your comfort zone into a new direction, sometimes better and sometimes not. Technology, obviously, is changing almost faster than we can keep up with. In ICU, every week, there was a new med, piece of equipment, or way of charting to learn. I need to digress to show the changes I saw. In my last semester at Chico State (nursing school), I worked in a high-risk OB unit (delivering babies). I was like a staff member, delivering babies without a problem. They wanted to hire me, but I didn't want to stay in Oroville at that time. One day, a lady desperately wanting a baby delivered a stillborn. In the next room, at the same time, a sixteen-year-old had a healthy baby she didn't want to touch or look at. All of us wanted to switch babies but couldn't. Life is so very cruel at times.

I started at age twenty-three in the Bay Area, Pinole. I got a p.m. shift on a surgical floor. I was placed in charge of fifty beds within several weeks (because of my bachelor's degree), worked half an hour to one hour overtime every night, charting, and sometimes worked a double shift (sixteen hours). I felt completely out of synch and lost those first few weeks; thank God for caring, nurturing nurses who take the new hires under their wings and help and encourage. Egg custards in the refrigerator for patients were my dinner while charting late at night, or a Breakfast Jack from Jack in the Box by my house, on the way home, was another late-night dinner. For a time, I did another RN's job (while she recuperated from an elective surgery). I worked from one p.m. to nine p.m., admitting, teaching, and prepping patients for all the next day's surgeries. I loved it; it developed into my first love for teaching. I lived one and a half miles from work. I had two kittens that would greet me with an entire roll of toilet paper unrolled throughout the house, or they'd be curled up together, hugging each other in the bathroom sink. We had aides, orderlies, and LVNs with lesser numbers of RNs. It changed from team leading to one RN per five patients over the first year. ICU staffing became one RN per two patients. Now, LVNs are almost gone, CNAs are somewhat used, and there are many more male RNs, many being some of the most caring men I've ever met.

I quickly realized I'd chosen an apartment in a gang-infested area. One night after work, I heard a girl screaming outside at 12:30 a.m. I grabbed a baseball bat and was going to go out and club her attacker. As I stepped out into the street, I saw a man with a gun standing in the street about 200 yards away. I went back in and called 911, never to rush out again lest the bad guy's weapon of choice be something more powerful than my bat. Patients in the Bay Area, in 1978, smoked in halls and rooms. It was allowed. We would see a man with a wheelchair, pulling his oxygen tank while smoking a cigarette and walking down the hallway. We now know you can literally set your oxygen on fire and burn your face. We frequently saw post-op narcotized patients in a four-bed room fall asleep with cigarettes burning to their fingertips and ash and embers smoldering in their sheets. I don't know how we never had a fire, except the nurses were on constant vigilance for it. Patients smoked marijuana in their rooms and thought we didn't know. I left work

Debra Bauguess

one night, and my car (second-hand Ford Maverick) wouldn't start. The battery cables had been cut so my battery could be taken out. It was so aggravating to have to buy cables and a battery.

Next, I got married to my college boyfriend, and we went to Mount Shasta. I went from eleven dollars an hour to four-teen dollars an hour and worked in a four-bed ICU/CCU and started on the p.m. shift (3:00–11:30 p.m.). I did days, nights, p.m.'s, and sometimes several shifts eight hours apart (double backing) as staffing dictated. Small-town life was glorious. Everybody was nice and waved to you, no matter how far out on some back road you were. We bartered for goods. My husband and I helped pour a concrete foundation for a house, and they gave us one-third of a butchered hog. To this day, that was the best pork I've ever had. We had no mall, no fast-food places, no stoplights, and no theater. We hiked and camped and felled trees for wood-burning stoves. I got adept at putting on chains in ten minutes to drive home in blizzards at 12:30 a.m. You never wanted to be behind a semitruck in pouring rain or heavy snow because it was a whiteout, and you could see nothing.

Our hospital literally sat at the base of Mount Shasta, and the birthing rooms that faced east looked square out on that glorious view. We used to have volcano drills for what to do if it erupted. We felt tremors quite often. When ICU was slow, I worked the medical-surgical floor, delivered babies, or once, even gavage fed (pushed ten ml. of special baby liquid food through a tiny feeding tube in the nose) a tiny baby every hour while rocking in a chair. I helped with traumas and code blues (people whose heart or breathing has stopped) and violent patients in the emergency room. Only one RN worked the ER, usually, but if something came in and she needed help, she always called me to come to help her. When needed, I drove patients and their kids, who lived in the same town, home in snowstorms if they had no transportation. There were no taxis or Ubers in the mountains. One MD did house calls and sat by the bedside of their dying patients. Nurses ran off roads when they hit black ice on their way to work. My husband was unemployed, and we lived on the veggies from our garden. We bought food only on sale and no meat or alcohol.

We lived with wood heat (great for power outages because you could heat water and cook on your wood stove). One winter, we hadn't gotten wood in yet, and a snowstorm hit, and we both got the flu. We lived in our warm waterbed for three days until a local brought us one and a half cords of cedar. The house, which was freezing, became warm and cozy. I still prefer wood heat to any other heat because it penetrates into your bones and comforts you. We rented and started at Lake Shastina in the high desert with sage and juniper, and coyotes. We then moved to our fairytale wood house (in Castella) with white lace curtains, thirty yards from the Sacramento River (in our back yard). We had tons of blackberries, rattlesnakes, and a three-foot deep, fast-moving river to fish in and tube down. Ten pan-sized trout with onions, potatoes, and eggs were frequent Saturday a.m. breakfasts. I miss that.

One winter, it rained for nine days straight, and I got a call at work that our house was going to flood; the river was rising one foot per hour. I had one stable ICU patient, and the MD let me transfer him to the regular nursing floor. I don't remember the half-hour drive home through pouring rain. Upon getting home, I walked through a foot of water in our yard, and my husband and I panicked. We put stuff up on tables

Debra Bauguess

and chairs, threw everything important we could find in our car and our VW bus, and then grabbed our golden retriever and cat. We drove through one and a half feet of water on the bridge over Castle Creek and made it to a local store's overhang just off Interstate 5. We parked both cars under it, started praying for our house, and slept in our bus with the two pets. It stopped raining at midnight. We went home the next a.m. to find the houses on either side of us flooded, but our house was untouched. The flood line was one inch below our lowest entry point. I know God stopped the rain; my mom and brother were home on their knees, praying for us. We had two car engines blow up, a flood, moved three times, and a reckless teen without a license ran his motorcycle through a stop sign into my car and broke his leg. His father found out we had insurance and sued us, but the jury unanimously acquitted me as not at fault (that trial took place over one whole year).

My time in the mountains ended when my husband beat me up and tried to kill me. I realized then that I had put all my energy into our marriage and had no life or friends and had been manipulated for several years. I know he loved me, but I was blind to what a normal good marriage should look like. By God's grace, I escaped with my life. My ex was lost, scared, and homeless for some time, but at least he is now on meds, living in a Bay Area "home," with food, shelter, and clothing at the state's expense. I've not had further contact with him since 1984.

After six months of depression (staying with my folks), I moved to Sacramento and a little duplex near Mercy San Juan Hospital. I started on eight-hour p.m. shifts in a six-bed CCU unit and then went to twelve-hour days and became a coronary-care unit supervisor. I was on many committees, teaching

Advanced Cardiac Life Support, and helped start the code-blue committee at work. Chris, another RN, and I standardized and stocked all the crash carts in the hospital (used for all emergencies). They were all full of different supplies before this. I think we restocked about thirty-six carts over several days. Our CCU moved to a temporary building with an eleven-bed CCU. I started working four hours a week in a cardiology office with three MDs, doing dobutamine stress tests in the office. I grew more confident, as many things happened there, like ventricular tachycardia, codes, rapid atrial fibrillation, and supraventricular tachycardia. I was the only RN usually also. For about fifteen plus years, I went to every code blue in the hospital when I was on and learned so very, very much about our, human, role in saving a life. I learned that when the Lord decides to take you, there's nothing we can do that will change that. CCUs then closed around the nation due to the new stenting of coronary arteries in MIs.

We moved to neuro, and I had to be the "old dog that learns new tricks." My later-life learning curve had just started when I was at the top of my game with hemodynamics and CCU nursing. We also had another hospital merge with ours, and many of our positions changed. I was placed back at the bedside and relieved of my supervisor duties; someone with more experience took my place. It ended up being a gift from the Lord, though. I remained at the patients' bedside until my last day in nursing. It's where I was most used. We were then making about seventy dollars an hour on day shift. I saw team nursing come and go, policies come in and go out, procedures and lines appear and disappear, and charting increase exponentially. Hospitals became more about staying solvent through cost containment. Charting changed from paper to computer and is now so time-consuming that it affects your time with patient care. They keep increasing what you need to chart because "if you don't chart it, it wasn't done." It's all about audits and proof that you did the smallest things so the insurance companies would reimburse the hospital. I understand the needs of the hospital to stay open, but the heart of nursing is the nurse–patient relationship, and human interaction lacks time as rules, policies, and charting increase. Patient satisfaction was scrutinized, as they think satisfied patients come back to our hospital and tell others about it, which means more revenue.

I always saw the need for patient safety as *first*. If the patient survived, make them feel cared for. You are not going to make an entitled, drug-seeking, suicidal, drug-withdrawing, or mentally ill patient satisfied. Nursing has changed drastically, somewhat for the better, but is much more aimed at patient satisfaction instead of prioritizing patient safety and well-being through great nursing care unhindered by hours a day on a computer. It's still a wonderful profession, and I would choose it all again, the good and the bad, but the gentle art of caring needs to be rediscovered. It's our world system that is changed to everything being about money instead of love. Maybe, someday, they will have the charting change from what needs to be audited to "what I did to help my patient and family today." You cannot hug, listen, or hold a hand if the state wants every minute of your day accounted for in a computer. I also see many RNs go into the profession for the money, now that it pays well. I am truly blessed for the pension I have and the money I made, but my job was *never* about the money; it was about the human being in that bed. It's very sad, to me, that you go to work in a place where there are desperately hurting people and that you may do a very good, efficient job but miss out on the connection that could be made with another's life.

> *"Love the Lord your God with all your heart and with all your soul and with all your strength and with all your mind; and, 'Love your neighbor as yourself.'"*
>
> — Luke 10:27

TEACHING MOMENT

Life keeps moving forward, and change will happen. Don't fight it. Learn and accept it, and it will go much more easily. Change can be good or bad; just stay true to who you are as a caregiver and do your best.

Debra Bauguess

THINGS I WON'T MISS

- Wrestling with combative patients.

- Waiting alone in the hallway with a sick patient with multiple lines for CT or interventional radiology.

- Things you need in an emergency not hooked up or missing (oxygen, suction, four-by-fours).

- Not having a twenty-five-year-old brain to multitask.

- Nursing station behind you with several (four or five) people talking and laughing loudly while your patient is grieving or dying.

- Three trips to MRI or CT in one shift.

- An IV pump that keeps alarming "air bubble."

- Trying to get an MD to understand an issue with the patient who you know needs to be addressed.

- The patient who wants ice is in the room the furthest from the nutrition room (where the ice is).

- The same six visitors go in and out of locked doors every ten minutes (what are they doing?). We have to answer the visitor-call system continuously on busy days.

- Spiking an IV bag, and it pierces through at the entrance, and the IV leaks out all over you or on the floor.

- Anything that splatters.

- Starting with two patients, both go out, and two new ones come in (all on one shift).

- When you change the entire bed and bathe the patient, and as you roll out the clean sheets and pads, the patient poos all over the clean sheets.

- When you look outside your room doorway to ask for help with clean up and the hallway is completely empty of people.

- Watching someone die in front of you, who shouldn't be dying, and feeling utterly helpless to stop it.

Debra Bauguess

NO MORE

- No more cold 05:30 a.m.'s. But no more saving a life at 07:15.

- No more going to work in the dark and coming home in the dark. But no more sunrises against the Sierras or sunsets to guide me home in the west.

- No more holidays and weekends missed with family. But less family to be with.

- No more free doughnuts, See's Candies, cookies, and potlucks. But no more weight gain from things I don't buy, only from what I bake.

- No more aching back, arms, feet, and knees from lifting and pulling. But more aching back, arms, feet, and knees from yard work or camping and hiking.

- No more trips to X-ray, CT, and MRI with heavy patients. But no more being able to look at a CT, CXR, or MRI and know what I'm seeing.

- No more telling family about a loved one's tragic or grim prognosis. But no more telling a family of a loved one's miraculous (supernatural) recovery.

- No more protein bars, V8, saltines, or pudding cups and coffee to keep me going. But all of the above only if I want it. Not to have to squeeze it into a five-minute lunch at 4 p.m. to keep myself from passing out on a crazy day.

- Nor more interrupted or missed breaks and lunches. But one long break with my bucket list.

- No more writing with symbols and abbreviations. But somehow, I still do it in my private journals.

- No more intellectual repartee and challenges. But a chance to learn more in a variety of things like photography and writing.

- No more broken nails or cracked, bleeding fingers from alcohol foam and washing hands 200 times a day. But maybe some dirt left under nails from planting more flowers.

- No more "get up, go to work, come home, sleep, and repeat." But more getting to see and spend time with *all* my friends and have people over.

- No more thirteen-hour days running nonstop and coming home exhausted beyond words. But no more feeling like I did my very best with my knowledge and expertise to save lives.

- No more cafeteria food. But more experimental recipes that may flop.

- No more wrestling with combative patients where I get kicked, punched, bitten, scratched, or spat on. But *no* "buts": more time with loving, caring family and friends.

- No more phone calls at 04:00 a.m. to come to work. But *no* "buts": sleep or not as I choose!

- No more fascinating dialogue or medical knowledge learned through endless questions answered by MDs. But even though that chapter is closed, more prayer time with God and increased growth in the Bible.

- No more fighting with a patient who's altered to keep them safe (lines in and them in the bed). But curling up with my purring cat on my lap and a good book.

- No more stress from three times the work with students stretching me and asking questions I can't answer. But no more teaching them that these people in the bed are valuable human beings to love and no more giving them my years of wisdom.

- No more deathbed hugging, crying, and praying with families and patients. But no more hugging, crying, and praying with patients and families. I *will* find a way to fill the void.

- No more mandatory learning of dry policies. But the choice to learn what affects me positively and about subjects I love.

- No more charting endless notes for the state to audit. But much more journaling, writing books, and writing letters to friends.

- No more days where I realize I had one cup of coffee and didn't go to the bathroom in twelve hours. But plenty of fluids when I want and an always-unlocked bathroom.

- No more smells of various body fluids. But smells I choose: flowers in the garden, the pine-scented woods on a hike, the salt air from the ocean, or a freshly-baked pie.

- No more crying after a hard emotional day full of hard things seen. But still crying upon hearing the sad news of increased world starvation, disasters, sex trafficking, child and animal abuse, and homelessness.

- No more requesting time off for holidays: Mother's day, birthdays, vacations, or events. But now I can go anywhere, anytime, any day or month I want!

Debra Bauguess

WHERE IS THE COFFEE?

I promised a couple of long-time buddies in MRI I would write this chapter. In the early years, I existed on egg custards, puddings, packaged broth powders, and graham crackers. Every nursing station has a refrigerator for the patients. To contain costs over the years, hospitals eventually did away with everything. Those egg custards were my only dinner for the first one and a half years. Seven Up, pudding, juice, and Grahams were around many years. We used to keep hot-cereal packets and cold-cereal boxes. In later years, I lived on saltines with little peanut butter and jelly packets, mostly due to missed lunches on twelve-hour shifts. The real juice that came in many varieties became cranberry and apple only and looked and tasted watered down and fake. Grahams and peanut butter and jelly went away, as well as margarine and bread, which we used to have. Plain turkey sandwiches remained with popsicles, sugar-free Jell-O, sugar-free pudding, and saltines. We did have packets of bouillon. The only thing that was sacred to shift work besides cold, clear water was coffee and/or tea. We changed from cafeteria coffee to unit coffee machines. We went through a variety of different coffee makers, from cheap ones to ones people brought from home to Keurigs, and then finally, one that took little packets of coffee to give you a cup. That was okay if they gave us enough for it to actually be there to use when we desperately needed it. We had coffee runs to the cafeteria or Starbucks for those needing it. I rarely drank more than one hot cup a day. I sometimes needed half a cup at my biorhythmic "downtime" between three and four p.m. I would be so sleepy, and my eyes were so heavy that half a cup would get me through to the end of the shift. I couldn't drink more than that or at any later time, or I wouldn't sleep once I got home. I usually only had one and a half to two hours to myself before bedtime after work. The coffee was for visitors staying long hours at a loved one's bedside and hospital staff. Patients frequently could not have it.

The snacks were the patients' but saved us from missed meals. Once your blood sugar drops and/or you're dehydrated, you'd get irritated and can't think straight. Personally, I don't think any department should ever cut back on or ration the coffee if they want awake, alert nurses and caregivers. This became a chapter idea as I sat in a cool MRI room with two friends while my patient underwent a forty-five-minute scan. I was sleepy, tired, and chilly. I asked if there was coffee anywhere. They said they'd run out of their allotment. Shame on you, hospitals!

Don't skimp on the caffeine if you want hardworking, fast-thinking, alert, and on-the-ball care teams! The different shift hours (especially nights), long hours, lack of food in missed breaks, and lost sleep over noisy neighbors or time changes add up to giving the nurses and hardworking, lifesaving staff their coffee/tea. Please, please don't cut back on the coffee. It's bad enough you couldn't have water or anything to drink near your workstation. Many of us were dehydrated much of the time. It's not an infection-control issue when it's capped, and we wash our hands 200-plus times a day. You can be assured anyone on the administrative floor probably had their coffee in abundance and water right next to them as they worked. The different floors even brought their own teas and

Debra Bauguess

coffees in much of the time. For the sake of one patient's life, couldn't the hospital spring for a "cup of joe" for a tired nurse who needs to be on her A game at three p.m. after struggling to keep her patient alive all day? Does the rationing apply to the CEO or administration or MDs? Please think about the lives saved by alert nurses instead of the few dollars lost on coffee. All I ask is to let us drink water to stay hydrated and some coffee when we haven't had sleep if you want safe patient care.

TEACHING MOMENT

Not all caregivers drink coffee, but the point is to keep your mind clear, alert, and awake, knowing that at any given moment, a crisis can happen with your patient. You can*not* let your guard down in ICU at any time. When you least expect it, things happen, and you must be on your A game at all times. A cup of something warm or with caffeine, after many hours on your feet, can help keep you sharp.

GOING OUT WITH COVID-19 (HEROES ARE REAL) AND SAYING GOODBYE

The last two years were the hardest. I had my second knee surgery (one on each) and fought more internal battles as I worked on while dealing with my own major family illnesses and issues requiring money, time, and emotional strength. Using emotional strength at home makes giving more emotional strength at work hard. Your well can run dry from time to time. I worked through mild flus, colds, body aches, sprained ankles, post-op knee surgeries, and abdominal cramping (from illness, bad food, or female cramps). I worked with headaches and vertigo, where I would hold onto walls as I walked and put ice packs on my neck and back when sitting. I had lumbar and cervical (low back and neck) radiologic changes from arthritis and forty-two years of lifting that left me with a back that would go out at any given moment. I had a reaction to a fruit cup with preservatives one a.m. and ended up in the ER, getting subcutaneous epinephrine with a heart rate of 160. I had an itching scalp, soles of my feet, and palms of my hands. My throat felt thick, and I had large hives appearing everywhere. I always kept Tylenol, Motrin, and Benadryl with me at work for allergic reactions (they happened three times at work) and body aches and pains.

Before my two knee surgeries, I limped for about six or seven months prior to each one. I honestly wonder how I made it, looking back. I worked through depression. I was called the "Ice Queen" during my first six months in 1984 due to having been beaten, almost killed, and then going through a divorce. I didn't know that until an engineer I dated and deeply cared for told me. I worked two-to-eight-hour shifts in a row several times and worked eighteen hours once with a day RN coming in at 03:00 a.m. (God bless you, Van). When you are young, you can do it. Overtime was frowned upon but usually happened because you got a critical admit right at the end of the shift, someone declined, needing lines, or a code blue at shift end. I worked eight-hour days, then an eight-hour night, then an eight-hour p.m. once at Mount Shasta while a fellow RN, Jim, worked the opposite p.m., day, and night. We each got about four or five hours of sleep in between each shift. Toward the end, as I aged, I found it harder and harder to sleep. My easiest shift always was three p.m. to midnight, where I'd go to bed at two a.m. and get up at 10:00, do banking and chores and exercise, and go back to work. Night shift workers are heroes. I only did some here and there and eight-hour nights for one month at Woodland ICU. I felt actually nauseous after a month of nights. Rarely I actually got seven hours of sleep. More often, it was between two to six hours. As I aged, I needed seven to eight hours every night, and it wears down on you as you lose the rest.

When COVID-19 hit, our unit became one of two Covid units (ICUs). I was sixty-five years old and had asthma, so they gave me all other types of patients since I had two risk factors increasing my chance of getting a severe case of it. I used to worry that my coworkers would dislike me for not being

Debra Bauguess

in "those rooms." I never refused to care for them; I just got assigned to the many others who did not have Covid. Seeing friends I cared about risk their lives to don scarce amounts of proper PPE (personal protective equipment) and go into the rooms of desperately ill, dying ventilated Covid-positive patients with multiple lines, anasarca (total body swelling), and proning (turning the patient face down in the bed to help the lung oxygenation) changed me.

Heroes are real, and they are my coworkers. I lived for four months through it with them and saw the exhaustion, resignation, frustration, and dogged courage it took to enter that room eighty times a day, putting on and taking off multiple pieces of gear and protection. They started calling in sick and were scared for their families at home, especially those with babies, small children, or elderly infirm parents. I know many stripped in the garage and showered before ever touching anyone at home. Many did not see their kids for months except from the other side of the glass or from a bike or car as they rode past (kids with the ex-wife).

Every a.m., they stopped us on entry and took our temps, and you were asked, "Have you traveled to any other countries or had aches, pains, extreme tiredness, shortness of breath, or cough?" Since I'd left at eight p.m. the night before and was now back at 06:30 a.m., I tried and said, "Yes, I have aches, pains, a headache, am tired, and have my asthma cough, can I go home?" "Oh no," they'd say, "we need you." I saw what Covid did to staff: it wore them down, and courage changed to extreme exhaustion and frustration, as all they did was take Covid patients. My heart goes out to *all* of them. I know I worked in a Covid unit and through the pandemic but didn't go through what they did. I wish every ICU Covid RN and respiratory therapist and MD who went into those rooms a million times would get a medal. The thanks from America were heartwarming and often brought me to tears. I saw respiratory therapists rapidly don PPE and spend hours in a room, adjusting and fine-tuning ventilator settings to try and give more oxygen to severely damaged lungs, all the while remaining cheerful, upbeat, and loving. One, K., has a heart of gold and was a friend and encourager when I was hurting. Several were like that, each special, kind, and loving in their own ways to befriend, help, and be there for you when you needed it. *You know who you are.* I was going to list names, but it would fill several pages. I love each and every one of you. You all played a role in my life. There are so many after forty-two years.

Saying goodbye to people you've been through highs and lows, crazy stress, life and death, and everything in between is hard. MDs, therapists, colleagues, and nurses all deserve a hug and a thank-you for who you are and what you meant to me. I feel older and wiser and am now the most giving I've ever been. Because of my pension and social security, I now make more than when I was working. I have time now to seek out those needing help and give what I can to help. Even though I was told one night that a group of people was talking about me, thinking I was not helpful, too weak, too slow, and easily stressed, I decided to go out strong. After a short time of disappointment and hurt, I prayed and decided to rise up above it. After all, I have forty-two years of knowledge and wisdom, multiple jobs in nursing, multiple people and patients who *do* love me, and the strength, through God, to overcome and forgive. Life is too short.

I had my last one or two years to push through the aging aches and stresses and become who I'd always wanted to be, the most caring bedside nurse I could be. I loved teaching, loved ICU, and loved the patients and their families. I started to work on always being happy, asking others if they needed help and only asked when I really needed it. I worked on relationships with every person I came into contact with, learned about their lives, and wrote personal, heartfelt notes to every single MD and staff member in my unit. I focused on the patient in the bed and poured my love into them. I grew to care deeply about neuro ICU, even though that was once the only type of ICU nursing I never wanted. It's complex and so very fascinating. The ones who thought I was slow and got stressed easily and asked for help a lot will find out at age sixty-five, after forty-two years in ICU (with arthritis), the toll aging takes. The ones who thought I was weak for getting too involved (as I came out of a room with tears)—you missed out—on an intimate, beautiful moment between myself and a patient or family member where I let God use me to pour a piece of my soul into their hurt and need, to bond over love given and received. I ultimately am the winner of a life well spent in the caring art of nursing.

To all those left behind: please search your hearts to find your reason for working. Is it money or to actually make a difference in a hurting person's life? You have the choice: to find lifelong joy and peace in a job well done or frustration and tiredness in a long day at work. It took me my entire nursing career to see this. I've made plenty of mistakes and had many hard moments with MDs, fellow nurses, patients, and families, but it's what you do with that learned knowledge that changes you. Hindsight is worth so much more.

I've tried to write only about the encouraging things, not the hundreds of other "teaching" moments. These few stories are only a hundred or so of thousands I have. Each one has a place in my heart. I would honestly not change a thing. It's not how fast you move or how much money you make; it's how much you *give* of your heart, soul, wisdom, caring, and love that changes your life and the ones you touched. I love ICU nursing; I always will, and I regret nothing.

> *"Greater love has no one than this: to lay down one's life for one's friends."*
>
> — John 15:13

> *"Love one another. As I have loved you, so you must love one another. By this everyone will know that you are my disciples, if you love one another."*
>
> — John 13:34–35

> *"I have brought you glory on earth by finishing the work you gave me to do."*
>
> — John 17:4

TEACHING MOMENT

Find heroes, emulate them. Use them to challenge yourself. We are not all created the same. People who hurt you and people who inspire you both make you become who you are. Use it to learn what not to be like or what to aspire to be like. You will see the best and worst of humanity; let it shape you into someone who rises above it all.

Debra Bauguess

WAS IT WORTH IT?

Knowing what I know now, of course, it's all worth it. My heart is full of memories and stories and people's faces that all touched my heart. Making a career decision to help people changed into something I could have never imagined. It was never for the money. It was *all* about being my passion and a mission field.

The first one and a half years in the Bay Area and four and a half in Mount Shasta, I grew and learned and soaked all lessons up like a sponge. The next thirty-six years in one hospital became a continuous learning ground and confidence builder, comfort-level stretcher, strength discoverer, teacher (on empathy and compassion), and hugging ministry. I learned you can put up with anything, no matter how stressful, irritating, or challenging, when it's only twelve hours. I learned who to ask and when to ask for help; double-checking does increase as you age. I learned it's rare to find a patient I cannot reach and rare to find a doctor without some redeeming qualities. I learned life is short and the days are ordained by our Creator, no matter what technology we use to intervene. I learned every patient is loved by God, so I could and did care deeply about all of them. I learned everyone (from MDs to nurses) makes mistakes, and by the grace of God, I never harmed anyone. I learned you can go thirteen hours without food, water, or a bathroom break. I learned *all* human life is worth saving. I learned it hurts to care, but the act of touching someone's life brings inexpressible joy. I learned that you should cherish each interaction with a fellow human being because you always learn something and get something out of it. I learned the joy of obeying when God prompted me by hugging a stranger, kissing a forehead, going into a stranger's room to talk with a distraught or lonely visitor, giving coffee, water, or money to someone hungry or thirsty, and going outside my comfort zone to ask, "How are you dealing with this?" "Do you understand?" or "How are you feeling?" That question always opened the floodgates, and forty-five minutes later, after hugs and tears, we both became "the ministered to."

When I listened, cared, and gave, I got back tenfold. I learned to take deep breaths and whisper prayers before giving hard news or answering a call light for the ninety-eighth time. I learned there is *no* excuse for rudeness or unkindness—*ever*. I learned most MDs and nurses and other team members truly care; we each have different gifts and strengths. I learned that my attitude always changed by the end of the shift (for the better). I learned that doctors can be respected peers as well as good friends. I learned respect and trust work both ways. I learned to notice and thank *every* hardworking team member. I learned that love only expands and grows and becomes stronger and, at some level, links us all. I learned the privilege of becoming a part of someone's life or death is only seen by the heart if you search for it. I learned bad things happen to good people, and sometimes there are no answers to "why?" I learned faith gives hope and hope takes away fear when someone is suffering or dying. I learned gentleness is the great icebreaker and comforter. I learned words aren't always needed, but touch and hugs are. I learned the small things mean the most. I learned the gratitude of a nurse I helped, a life I saved, or thanks from a patient, family, or MD is what kept me going.

Debra Bauguess

I learned that the sun still comes up tomorrow and that time does heal. I learned that true grief paralyzes, but a kindness shown, through words or touch, brings light into the darkness. I learned the value of owning my mistakes and learning from them, *never* to repeat them. I learned the value of a hot shower or glass of wine or pet on my lap after a hard day worked wonders. I learned you can't help or fix every person or situation. I learned the human body is a miracle in itself due to its power to regenerate, heal, and survive the most devastating of circumstances or injuries. I learned that intensive care is actually *intense*. I learned I will always cry at the miracle of a baby being born. I learned not to take for granted my patient would be there the next day. Say what you feel today. I learned it's okay to be afraid and not know how to do something: just be honest and do your best. I learned dignity and self-worth: do not let a patient, nurse, MD, or management tear you down if you are not in the wrong. Stick up for yourself when right. I learned human life is fragile and yet strong and complex. I learned the big strong ones can be fearful of a subcutaneous injection or Band-Aid being pulled off, but a truly ill, suffering, and dying patient could minister to you as they die with courage and strength. These are the things I'll never forget. In forty-two years, I knew thousands of people and may have had a hand in saving a thousand lives, but the remarkable part was the trust put in me and the love that flowed both directions over and over again. It's the only thing that keeps our world going.

Was it worth the chronic pain I now live with, the back that goes out, the neck pain, the shoulder pain, and the aching knees? Yes, a million times, *yes*! Human life is precious, and we are all unique with different strengths and weaknesses. Some of us are given a privilege to pour into the lives of others and bring love, caring, hope, encouragement, and help in times of need. Whether you are a paramedic/EMT, firefighter, chaplain, police, teacher, or healthcare professional, we *all* have been given the gift of taking another person's hands and walking with them through the fire to the best of our God-given ability.

Nursing is not for the squeamish, the overly sensitive (can't take criticism), the infirm, the quick to anger, the rude or unkind, or anyone who does not or cannot deal with any/all personality types. We see egotistical, entitled, racist, biased, angry, out-of-control (drugs, mental illness), demeaning, superior, judgmental, needy, panicked, hurting, grieving, violent people. We also see loving, trusting, respectful, caring, uplifting, strong, courageous, inspiring, giving, humble, open-hearted, silly, helpful, beautiful human beings. They are all worthy of our love and caring, and we should evaluate whether or not we are worthy of giving it.

Nursing is the hardest job I've ever loved and the *only* profession I would choose all over again if asked.

> *"For I know the plans I have for you,' declares the*
> LORD, *'plans to prosper you and not to harm you, plans*
> *to give you hope and a future.'"*
>
> — Jeremiah 29:11

TEACHING MOMENT

I guarantee you will receive if you pour out. Caregiving is *not* just a job. Human beings are precious, fragile creatures needing love and care. Be the one who gives of yourself, and you will know it was *all* worth it in the end.

Debra Bauguess

REFLECTIONS
ON NURSING

Yes, you know they want another cup of ice chips, but the man they brought in last night has just messed himself for the fifth time today, and his daughter is visiting him from out of town, so...

Meanwhile, a patient needs to go to the bathroom.

Two families are calling for status updates.

One patient has just pulled out their ET tube, art-line, and central line—with restraints on.

A doctor is making his rounds.

Three heart monitors are showing increased arrhythmias and low blood pressures.

You haven't used the bathroom for twelve hours and have had one cold cup of coffee all day.

You are overwhelmed.

The cafeteria is closed, and you missed lunch.

You just washed your hands for the 97th time today.

You just got told you know nothing by a person who didn't pass the tenth grade.

You literally cannot get the IV pump to stop beeping.

And you just lost your favorite patient.

Meanwhile, your patient is ringing the buzzer nonstop for a cup of ice chips, which you bring, and it's spilled into the sheets soaking them within five minutes, and now they want more ice chips—and a dry bed.

— Written partly by Scott Randall and partly by myself

HOSPITAL, I'M DONE

I'm not nostalgic regarding all that stuff; for forty long years, I was tough enough, responding to emergencies with expertise. Now I would rather visit mountains, rivers, and trees.

— Written by my friend Pete Hupp, RN

NURSING

Never be bored, always be challenged, and sometimes frustrated. You have an immense responsibility and very little authority. As you step into people's lives to make a difference, some will bless you, and some will curse you. You'll see people at their worst and at their best. You'll never cease to be amazed at the human's capacity for love, courage, and endurance. You'll cry a lot, laugh a lot, and know what it is to be human and humane.[2]

— Unknown author

"GOD MADE A NURSE"

In the beginning, God created the heavens and earth. He did this in seven days. Sometime after the eighth day, God saw that humans needed a special kind of person to take care of them. He needed someone to respond to a calling and hold the hand of other humans through the toughest of times. So God made a Nurse.

Debra Bauguess

*He knew we needed someone with the grit to
not get out of sorts at the sight of blood; to help people
survive heart attacks and strokes and catastrophes;
to keep a person alive with hoses, tubes and wires; to
hold it together when everyone else is falling apart,
no matter the situation; and give hope when there is
none. So God made a Nurse.*

*He needed someone who could explain complex
situations and procedures, but in a way grandpa could
understand it; monitor vital signs and tell the doctor
what the patient needs and when; calculate and know
the difference between milligrams and milliliters; hear
a heartbeat as both an algorithm and an emotion;
explain to a family that grandma is ready to go to
heaven when they want her to stay. So God made a
Nurse.*

*He needed someone to feed and bathe helpless peo-
ple when no one else would, on weekends and holidays
while others were sleeping. So God made a Nurse.*

*He wanted someone who could and would run
an IV pump, stick needles into veins with compassion, draw and flush fluids like a precision machinist;
wrestle a patient out of their mind into bed, have a
tolerant nose, and a stomach made of steel; to make
the broken whole and give a soothing word for weary
souls. So God made a Nurse.*[3]

— A poem by Lee Bond
(rendition of "God Made a Farmer"
by Paul Harvey)

ABILITY TO FIX

We may not have the ability to "fix" everyone, but we definitely have the capability and responsibility to have compassion for them, to make them comfortable, to be their advocate, and to be the person who comes into their room and makes them feel like a human being.[4]

— Christine Ehlers,
Chicken Soup for the Nurse's Soul

TOO OFTEN

Too often we underestimate the power of a touch, a smile, a kind word, a listening ear, an honest compliment, or the smallest act of caring, all of which have the potential to turn a life around.[5]

— Leo Buscaglia

FIRST TO WORK

Last to leave. […] a unique soul who will pass through your life for a minute and impact it for eternity. An empowered individual whom you may meet for only twelve hours, but who will put you and yours above themselves.[6]

— Anupam Kher

Debra Bauguess

CLOSE TO THE HAND OF GOD

I held the hand of a ninety-one-year-old woman as she took her last breath.

I heard the cries of an alcoholic patient with alcohol withdrawal syndrome as he begged for restraints to be removed.

I brushed the hair of a nineteen-year-old woman who lay silent in a coma.

I held in my arms a fragile infant who'd suffered head injuries when his mother's boyfriend threw him against a wall.

I inserted tubes to empty the stomach of a patient who attempted suicide because he couldn't find a reason to live.

I dried the tears of a twenty-three-year-old woman who was paralyzed from the neck down and grieving for her mother, who'd died in the same car accident.

And I laughed with the same young woman at the poster over her bed of a good-looking guy with great buns.

I sat outside the door of an AIDS patient while his mother watched him die, and I prayed for empathy and understanding.

I accompanied a body to the morgue and searched my soul for faith and hope.

The Person in the Bed

I bowed my head as the chaplain prayed with a family for comfort and peace.

I've felt joy at the miracle of reviving a life and helplessness in prolonging suffering.

I hear the rhythm of the ventilators and the alarms that call me.

I watch the lines on the cardiac monitors and measure them in milliseconds.

I mix, calculate, and titrate life-sustaining intravenous infusions and chart on flow sheets that seem to tell a story of it all.

I'm amazed at how a diseased body can live for many years and healthy one die in seconds.

I've marveled at the work of brain surgeons and seen them baffled by the complexity of a single life.

I've prayed silently over many patients as they lay suffering and at the mercy of the hands that care for them each day.

I've offered comfort to families who wait for days without rest, sustained by hope and prayer.

I've seen the rich and the poor, the Black and the white, and the ignorant and the educated become equals in the fight for life.

I've seen death often enough that I'm not so afraid of it.

I've been humbled and privileged to be this close to the hand of God.

Debra Bauguess

And in all of this, I've received a million times over what I've given.

I am a critical-care nurse.

— Carol Ann Cowey, RN

MY PLEA TO YOU

At the end of it all, I realized one constant gave me the courage and strength to love everyone and live a life worthy of my calling. He is my Lord and Savior, Jesus. Life is so very precious and short. Anything can happen at any time to any of us. Please consider your mortal soul and seek to find an answer to life after death. There is a very real, living, righteous God who sent His only Son to give His life to save us for an eternity with Him. Jesus rose from the dead after suffering and dying for all our sins: past, present, and future. He now sits in heaven at the right hand of His Father and will come back for those who believe in Him.

I am human and a sinner. He changed my life completely. He loves you, too. Please examine your beliefs. There is a choice for eternal life without pain, sorrow, or suffering. It's as simple as confessing any sins in your life, asking Jesus to forgive you, repenting of your sins, and believing He died for you and is the living Son of God. You then can be saved and redeemed. There will be an everlasting deep love as you've never felt before. You'll be assured of eternal life in heaven.

ENDNOTES

1 Abigail Van Buren, quoted in Goodreads, Inc., accessed January 2, 2022, https://www.goodreads.com/quotes/694900-just-for-today-i-will-live-through-this-day-only.

2 "Inside Scoop: Working in a Domestic Violence Shelter," Women's Advocates, July 13, 2020, https://www.wadvocates.org/2020/07/13/insidescoop_workingindvshelter.

3 Lee Bond, "God Made a Nurse" (rendition of "God Made a Farmer" or "Farmer" by Paul Harvey), quoted in Singing River Heroes, May 06, 2020, https://singingriverhealthsystem.com/2020/05/god-made-a-nurse.

4 Christine Ehlers, Jack Canfield, Mark Victor Hansen, *Chicken Soup for the Nurse's Soul: Stories to Celebrate, Honor and Inspire the Nursing Profession* (New York: Simon and Schuster, 2012), https://books.google.com/books?id=Vdn24itAt_4C.

5 Leo Buscaglia, quoted in BrainyQuote.com, BrainyMedia Inc., accessed January 2, 2022, https://www.brainyquote.com/quotes/leo_buscaglia_106299.

6 Anupam Kher, (@AnupamPKher) "Definition of Nurses," Twitter, December 10, 2020, https://twitter.com/anupampkher/status/1336891961400205313.

CPSIA information can be obtained
at www.ICGtesting.com
Printed in the USA
LVHW030526130522
718523LV00015B/343